D0553563

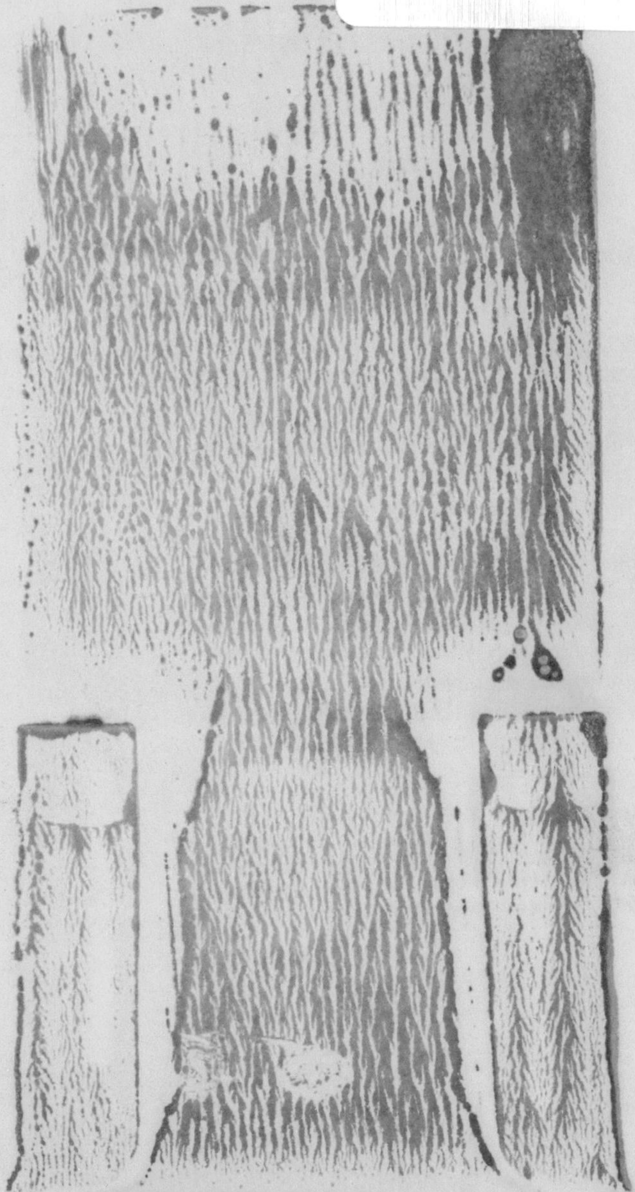

CHAMPLAIN COLLEGE

The Shape of Carbon Compounds

THE GENERAL CHEMISTRY MONOGRAPH SERIES

Russell Johnsen, Editor
Florida State University

Gordon M. Barrow (*Case Institute of Technology*)	THE STRUCTURE OF MOLECULES
Werner Herz (*Florida State University*)	THE SHAPE OF CARBON COMPOUNDS
Edward L. King (*University of Colorado*)	HOW CHEMICAL REACTIONS OCCUR
Bruce H. Mahan (*University of California, Berkeley*)	ELEMENTARY CHEMICAL THERMODYNAMICS
Gregory R. Choppin (*Florida State University*)	NUCLEI AND RADIOACTIVITY
Robin Hochstrasser (*University of Pennsylvania*)	SPECTRA, STRUCTURE, AND PHOTOCHEMISTRY OF ATOMS

The Shape of Carbon Compounds

An Introduction to Organic Chemistry

Werner Herz
Florida State University

1964
W. A. BENJAMIN, INC. New York Amsterdam

THE SHAPE OF CARBON COMPOUNDS
An Introduction to Organic Chemistry

Library of Congress Catalog Card Number 63-11725
Manufactured in the United States of America

Final manuscript was received on November 14, 1962;
this volume was published on May 15, 1963;
second printing, with corrections,
February 18, 1964.

The publisher wishes to acknowledge the assistance
of Galen Fleck, who edited the manuscript,
and Russell F. Peterson, who produced
the illustrations.

W. A. BENJAMIN, INC.
2465 Broadway, New York 25, New York

Editor's Foreword

THE TEACHING OF GENERAL CHEMISTRY to beginning students becomes each day a more challenging and rewarding task as subject matter becomes more diverse and more complex and as the high school preparation of the student improves. These challenges have evoked a number of responses; this series of monographs for General Chemistry is one such response. It is an experiment in the teaching of chemistry which recognizes a number of the problems that plague those who select textbooks and teach chemistry. First, it recognizes that no single book can physically encompass all the various aspects of chemistry that all instructors collectively deem important. Second, it recognizes that no single author is capable of writing authoritatively on *all* the topics that are included in everybody's list of what constitutes general chemistry. Finally, it recognizes the instructor's right to choose those topics which he considers to be important without having to apologize for having omitted large parts of an extensive textbook.

This volume, then, is one of approximately fifteen in the General Chemistry Monograph Series, each written by one or more highly qualified persons very familiar with the current status of the subject by virtue of research in it and also conversant with the problems associated with teaching the subject matter to beginning students. Each volume deals broadly with one of the subdivisions of general chemistry and constitutes a complete entity, far more comprehensive in its coverage than is permitted by the limitation of the standard one-volume text. Taken together, these volumes provide a range of topics from which the individual instructor can easily select those that will provide for his class an appropriate coverage of the material he considers most important.

Furthermore, inclusion of a number of topics that have only recently been considered for general chemistry courses, such as thermodynamics, molecular spectroscopy, and biochemistry, is planned and these volumes will soon be available. In every instance a modern structural point of view has been adopted with the emphasis on general principles and unifying theory.

These volumes will have other uses also: selected monographs can be used to enrich the more conventional course of study by providing readily available, inexpensive supplements to standard texts. They should also prove valuable to students in other areas of the physical and biological sciences needing supplementary information in any field of chemistry pertinent to their own special interests. Thus, students of biology will find the monographs on biochemistry, organic chemistry, and reaction kinetics particularly useful. Beginning students in physics and meteorology will find the monograph on thermodynamics rewarding. Teachers of elementary science will also find these volumes invaluable aids to bringing them up to date in the various branches of chemistry.

Each monograph has several features which make it especially useful as an aid to teaching. These include a large number of solved examples and problems for the student, a glossary of technical terms, and copious illustrations.

The authors of the several monographs deserve much credit for their enthusiasm which made this experiment possible. Professor Rolfe Herber of Rutgers University has been of invaluable assistance in the preparation of this series, having supplied editorial comment and numerous valuable suggestions on each volume. Thanks are also due to Professor M. Kasha of the Florida State University for many suggestions during the planning stages and for reading several of the manuscripts.

Russell Johnsen

Tallahassee, Florida
October 1962

Preface

THIS VOLUME is not intended as a textbook of organic chemistry for any single course. It was written in a flurry of enthusiasm for a project that seemed to me to have a good deal of merit—to afford beginning students of chemistry the opportunity to learn more about organic molecules than is given in the standard general chemistry textbook.

I have deliberately concentrated on one aspect of organic chemistry—structure—because it is most easily grasped. Moreover, I think that familiarity with this topic, more than any other, is important to the student who might not be exposed subsequently to formal courses in organic chemistry. If one wishes to understand, on a somewhat more sophisticated level than that adopted in newspaper supplements and magazines, what organic chemists do and why they do it, some knowledge of structural organic chemistry seems indispensable.

Mechanisms and functional group behavior have been touched upon only when necessary, and no attempt has been made to discuss organic nomenclature except through example. These subjects, I feel, can be profitably reserved for "the full treatment" given in second- and third-year chemistry courses, and I make no apologies for slighting them here.

WERNER HERZ

Tallahassee, Florida
January 1963

Contents

The Shape of Carbon Compounds

I

Introduction

THIS BOOK is an introduction to one of the most vigorous of scientific disciplines and one of the most remarkable achievements of the human intellect: organic chemistry, the chemistry of carbon compounds.

The merit of this statement is difficult to justify to someone who has not yet experienced the thrill of discovery, either personally by working in the laboratory or vicariously by reading the story as it unfolds in the works of the great organic chemists of the past and present.

Part of the difficulty is unfamiliarity with the language used by organic chemists. Perhaps a greater obstacle is ignorance of just what organic chemists do, how and why they operate, and what they seek to accomplish.

It is easy to point to the practical results of research by organic chemists. The role which plastics, artificial fibers, drugs, petroleum, rubber, and pesticides play in our daily lives is evident to everyone. Predictions of how chemical technology will free man from his present dependence on diminishing natural resources are grist for the mills of science-fiction writers.

However, we should not confuse these tangible present and future contributions of organic chemistry to civilization with the fundamental objective of organic chemists: to understand a certain part of man's material environment. The degree to which this understanding has progressed is the remarkable intellectual achievement referred to in the first paragraph.

To say that understanding has advanced does not mean that understanding has been reached. The vigor with which organic chemists pursue their work is a testimony to the dissatisfaction that they feel with their present state of knowledge, remarkable though it may be in comparison with the state of knowledge fifty or one hundred years ago. It is the objective of this book to impart to the reader a part—a very small part indeed—of this knowledge.

Let us first try to delineate the subject matter of organic chemistry. Even in the early days of chemical experimentation, scientists concerned themselves not only with rocks, the liquids, and the "vapors" of inanimate nature, but attacked with zest materials of animal and vegetable source. Curiosity persisted about the sweet and sour taste of certain foods, the remarkable physiological effects of certain plant extracts, and the composition of such metabolic products as urine and gallstones. Whether by accident or design, a number of well-defined substances had been isolated from plant or animal sources by the beginning of the nineteenth century.

At about that time, the principles of chemical analysis were being developed. It became apparent that only a few elements made up the compounds associated with living organisms. Some, like waxes, contained only carbon and hydrogen. Others, like acetic acid, sugar, and wood alcohol, were made up of carbon, hydrogen, and oxygen. Still others, like urea and morphine, were found to contain nitrogen also. In sharp contrast, substances of mineral origin contained a wide variety of different elements, metallic as well as nonmetallic, heavy as well as light.

The terms "organic" and "inorganic" were coined to distinguish the two classes of compounds. Originally, "organic" referred to a type of compound which could be isolated from either an animal or a vegetable source and which contained mainly carbon and hydrogen, with perhaps oxygen and/or nitrogen. As a rule these substances were readily combustible, easily destroyed by heat, and, frequently, sensitive to air or light. For a while it was assumed that organic compounds could arise only through the operation of a mysterious life force associated with living organisms, whereas inorganic compounds could be prepared artificially in the laboratory from their constituents or from other inorganic materials.[1]

It did not take long to discover that the so-called organic compounds could be transformed by laboratory operations into a multitude of other substances of which nature had apparently never dreamed. It also proved possible to convert some materials of mineral origin into compounds previously isolated from animal or vegetable sources without the agency of any living organism.

Our definition of organic compounds is therefore no longer limited to substances of biological origin. Instead, the term "organic" is applied to a group of compounds that exhibit a number of characteristic properties. All of them contain carbon; most of them contain hydrogen; and many of them contain oxygen, nitrogen, and some other element such as sulfur, a halogen, or phosphorus. The subject matter of organic chemistry is the study of all compounds of carbon, whether they are derived from some natural source or are purely synthetic.

[1] This process is known as synthesis.

II

The Shape of Molecules—Alkanes

ONE OF THE FEATURES which distinguishes organic compounds from most inorganic ones is combustibility. When brought near a flame, the organic compounds ignite and burn completely. What happens to the elements of which they are composed? The products of combustion are carbon dioxide, water, and, in some cases, oxides of nitrogen.

If a small sample of an organic substance, say, 3 to 4 mg of acetic acid, is weighed accurately and then burned in an elaborate apparatus and if the evolved gases are measured carefully, it is possible to determine the percentage of the various elements that make up a molecule of the substance. From this, a chemist can deduce an *empirical formula*. In the case of acetic acid, the empirical formula is CH_2O. This indicates that the atoms of carbon, hydrogen, and oxygen in a molecule of acetic acid are in the ratio 1:2:1.

By determining that the molecular weight of acetic acid is 60, we can proceed further and derive the molecular formula $C_2H_4O_2$. That is to say, a molecule of acetic acid is made up of two carbon atoms, four hydrogen atoms, and two oxygen atoms. What holds these atoms together? Are they held together in any particular way?

2–1 ISOMERISM

We shall defer discussion of the first question and deal immediately with the second. The answer is yes; the eight atoms of acetic acid *are* held together in a particular way.

There exists at least one other substance which has both the same empirical formula, CH_2O, and the same molecular formula, $C_2H_4O_2$, as acetic acid. This substance is called methyl formate. It is easy to distinguish between acetic acid and methyl formate. The two substances have different smells, different densities, and different boiling points, and they behave quite differently when exposed to the same chemical reagents.

We can explain this only if we assume that acetic acid and methyl formate molecules contain different arrangements of the same atoms. Acetic acid and methyl formate are said to be isomers, substances which have the same empirical formula but different arrangements of atoms or structures.

As the number of atoms in a given empirical formula increases, the number of possible arrangements becomes larger also. As the molecules become more complex, the number of possible isomers increases rapidly and, when we are dealing with elaborate giant molecules, verges on the astronomical. This accounts for the enormous number and variety of organic compounds.

```
          O                      O
         //                     //
CH3—C                   H—C
         \                      \
          OH                     O—CH3
```

acetic acid — methyl formate

two compounds of formula $C_2H_4O_2$ (isomers)

2–2 STRUCTURE OF METHYL ALCOHOL

Although one of the objectives of organic chemists is to determine the arrangement of atoms within molecules, it would be a superhuman task to attempt this for each of the known organic compounds, which number in the millions. Fortunately, these compounds can be arranged into a number of groups, or classes, whose members exhibit similar characteristics and hence, we assume, have similar structures. Thus, in dealing with a new or unexpected compound, the chemist's first aim is to study its behavior until he can assign it to one, or several, of the well-established classes. Another method of classifying it would be to convert it to a compound which has been studied previously and whose structure is known reasonably well.

The fundamental problem of structure can be illustrated by retracing the classic experiments devised by nineteenth-century organic chemists to determine the structure of methyl alcohol (also known as wood alcohol or methanol), which has the molecular formula CH_4O. They knew that methyl alcohol reacts with hydrogen bromide to yield methyl bromide and water:

$$CH_4O + HBr \rightarrow CH_3Br + H_2O. \quad (1)$$

Bromine displaces the oxygen and one hydrogen; the resulting substance CH_3Br is also known as bromomethane. The two displaced atoms appear as an —OH (hydroxyl) group in the water molecule and were apparently present as such in the molecule of methyl alcohol. This assumption is strongly supported by the observation that methyl bromide can be reconverted to methyl alcohol by boiling with sodium hydroxide solution (in which the —OH group is known to be present):

$$CH_3Br + NaOH \rightarrow CH_3OH + NaBr. \quad (2)$$

Furthermore, just like water, Eq. (3), methyl alcohol liberates hydrogen on treatment with sodium, Eq. (4):

$$HOH + Na \rightarrow HONa + \tfrac{1}{2}H_2 \quad (3)$$

$$CH_3OH + Na \rightarrow CH_3ONa + \tfrac{1}{2}H_2. \quad (4)$$

Of the four hydrogen atoms in methyl alcohol, only one (that attached to oxygen) seems to have been displaced.

We conclude that the hydroxyl group and three hydrogen

atoms are attached to carbon and that the so-called structural formula is

$$\begin{array}{c} \phantom{H-{}}H \\ \phantom{H-{}}| \\ H-C-O-H \\ \phantom{H-{}}| \\ \phantom{H-{}}H \end{array}$$

I

where the dashes, which we call bonds, stand for the forces that hold the atoms together.

In a similar manner, we can show that the substance ethyl alcohol, C_2H_6O, may be represented by structure II and not by structure III. In these structures we assume that carbon exhibits the valence of four to which we have become accustomed in simple molecules.

$$\begin{array}{ccccccc} & & H & & H & & \\ & & | & & | & & \\ H & - & C & - & C & - & O-H \\ & & | & & | & & \\ & & H & & H & & \end{array} \qquad \begin{array}{ccccccc} & & H & & & H & \\ & & | & & & | & \\ H & - & C & -O- & & C & -H \\ & & | & & & | & \\ & & H & & & H & \end{array}$$

II III

2-3 THE TETRAHEDRAL CARBON ATOM

The representations which we have derived for methyl and ethyl alcohol are inadequate for one very important reason. Although they indicate the order in which the various atoms are linked, they say nothing about the relative positions that the atoms occupy in space. We might actually draw the inference from them that the molecules are planar and that the bond angles are always 90° or 180°. This is not correct, as the following argument shows.

Treatment of bromomethane, obtained from methyl alcohol as shown in Eq. (1), with zinc in the presence of acid produces a substance of formula CH_4 called methane. In turn, methane can be converted back to bromomethane by exposure to bromine at high temperature:

$$CH_3Br \xrightarrow[H^+]{Zn} CH_4 \xrightarrow{Br_2} CH_3Br + HBr. \qquad (5)$$

Now regardless of how often we perform the experiment and how carefully we analyze the products, we never obtain more than the one compound of formula CH_3Br, bromomethane. This shows that it does not make any difference which of the four hydrogen atoms of methane is replaced by bromine (unless one is preferentially substituted every time[1]) and that all four hydrogens are equivalent.

Three spatial arrangements that satisfy this requirement are possible. The first (IV) is planar, with carbon at the center of a square or rectangle and the hydrogen atoms at the four corners.

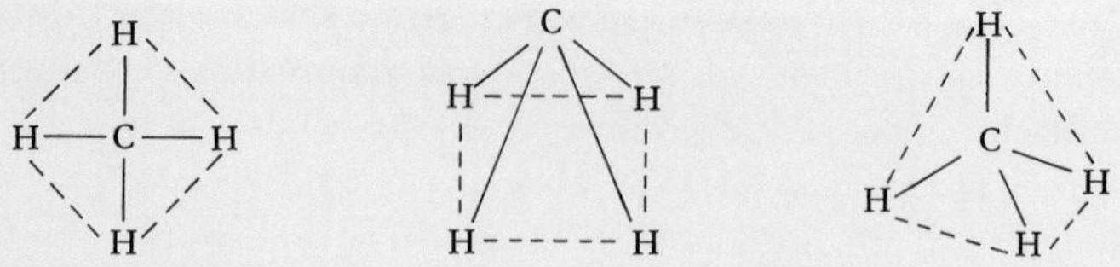

IV V VI

The second (V) is pyramidal, with carbon at the apex of the pyramid and the hydrogen atoms at the four corners of a square base. The third (VI) is tetrahedral, with carbon at the center of a tetrahedron and the hydrogen atoms at the four corners. Which of these three arrangements is correct?

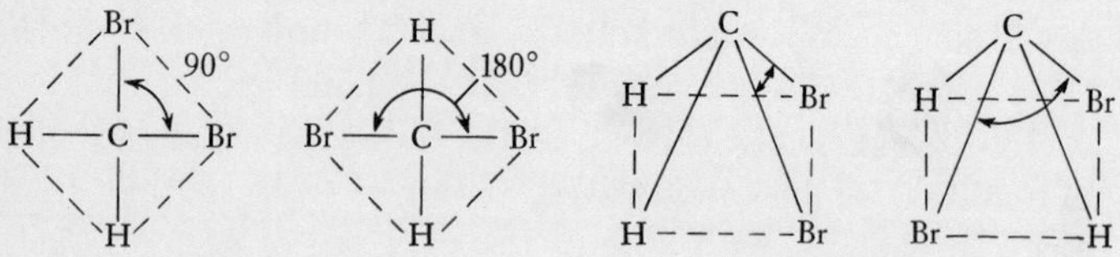

90° 180°

from IV from V

[1] This is an important reservation which cannot be dismissed lightly. The most convincing argument for the tetrahedral nature of the carbon rests on the phenomenon of optical isomerism, which is discussed in Chap. XI.

If bromomethane is treated once more with bromine, there is obtained one, and only one, substance of formula CH_2Br_2. Since one would expect two isomers from either IV or V (see diagrams), it is obvious that arrangement VI is the only one which harmonizes with the evidence. Hence the bonds that carbon forms with

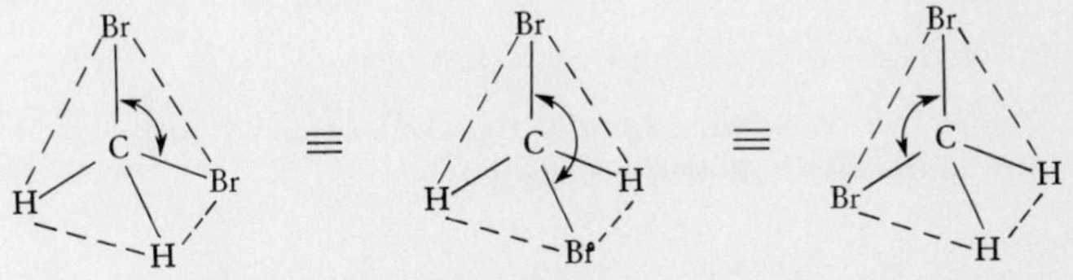

from VI

hydrogen, bromine, or indeed any other element W, X, Y, or Z in compounds of the type CH_3X, CH_2XY, CHXYZ, or CWXYZ are directed toward the corners of a tetrahedron, and we refer to the carbon atom as being tetrahedral. This deduction, which was reached on purely logical grounds by the Dutch chemist Van't Hoff in 1874, has been verified by the methods of X-ray diffraction, electron diffraction, and molecular spectroscopy.

2-4 CONFORMATIONS

As an example of the consequences which result from the tetrahedral nature of the carbon atom, let us consider an important class of organic compounds, the aliphatic hydrocarbons, or alkanes. These substances have the general formula C_nH_{2n+2}. It is clear that methane (Fig. 2–1) is the simplest representative of this series and that other members may be made up by successively replacing hydrogen atoms with carbon. In doing so we must keep in mind the requirement that carbon be tetravalent. In this manner we could write thousands of formulas only a few of which are illustrated. We also adopt, for the more complex hydrocarbons, so-called condensed formulas. In these, individual bonds are omitted except for vertical bonds between carbon atoms. Hydrogen atoms attached to a particular carbon atom are written to the immediate right of that carbon atom.

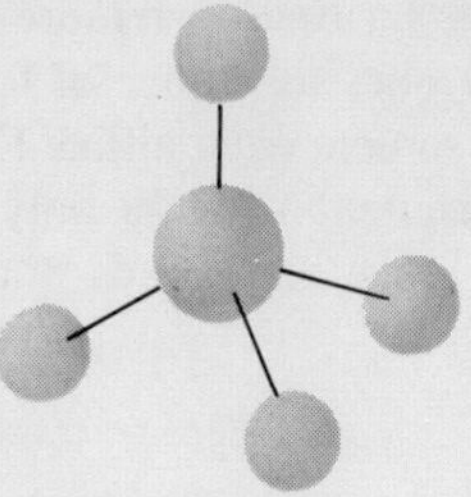

Figure 2–1 A frequently used representation of the methane molecule (ball-and-stick model).

$$\begin{array}{ccccccc} & & \mathrm{H} & & \mathrm{H} & & \\ & & | & & | & & \\ \mathrm{H} & - & \mathrm{C} & - & \mathrm{C} & - & \mathrm{H} \\ & & | & & | & & \\ & & \mathrm{H} & & \mathrm{H} & & \end{array} \quad \text{or} \quad CH_3CH_3$$

ethane
VII

$$\begin{array}{ccccccccc} & & \mathrm{H} & & \mathrm{H} & & \mathrm{H} & & \\ & & | & & | & & | & & \\ \mathrm{H} & - & \mathrm{C} & - & \mathrm{C} & - & \mathrm{C} & - & \mathrm{H} \\ & & | & & | & & | & & \\ & & \mathrm{H} & & \mathrm{H} & & \mathrm{H} & & \end{array} \quad \text{or} \quad CH_3CH_2CH_3$$

propane
VIII

$$\begin{array}{ccccccccccc} & & \mathrm{H} & & \mathrm{H} & & \mathrm{H} & & \mathrm{H} & & \\ & & | & & | & & | & & | & & \\ \mathrm{H} & - & \mathrm{C} & - & \mathrm{C} & - & \mathrm{C} & - & \mathrm{C} & - & \mathrm{H} \\ & & | & & | & & | & & | & & \\ & & \mathrm{H} & & \mathrm{H} & & \mathrm{H} & & \mathrm{H} & & \end{array} \quad \text{or} \quad CH_3CH_2CH_2CH_3$$

n-butane
IX

$$\begin{array}{ccccccccc} & & \mathrm{H} & & \mathrm{H} & & \mathrm{H} & & \\ & & | & & | & & | & & \\ \mathrm{H} & - & \mathrm{C} & - & \mathrm{C} & - & \mathrm{C} & - & \mathrm{H} \\ & & | & & | & & | & & \\ & & \mathrm{H} & & | & & \mathrm{H} & & \\ & & & & | & & & & \\ & & \mathrm{H} & - & \mathrm{C} & - & \mathrm{H} & & \\ & & & & | & & & & \\ & & & & \mathrm{H} & & & & \end{array} \quad \text{or} \quad \begin{array}{c} CH_3CHCH_3 \\ | \\ CH_3 \end{array}$$

isobutane
X

$CH_3CH_2CH_2CH_2CH_3$ — *n*-pentane XI

$CH_3CH(CH_3)CH_2CH_3$ — isopentane XII

$CH_3C(CH_3)_2CH_3$ — neopentane XIII

Now although these formulas are apparently planar and the sequence of carbon atoms is apparently linear, our discussion of the methane molecule has led us to the conclusion that the bonds emanating from carbon atoms point to the corners of a tetrahedron. Hence a more accurate representation for propane would be that of Fig. 2–2, which illustrates the tetrahedral angles (109°28′). In the higher-molecular-weight hydrocarbons, the carbon chain may be folded in various ways, as, for example, in *n*-pentane (Fig. 2–3), as long as the tetrahedral angles are maintained as shown. The different ways of folding the carbon chain are often referred to as "conformations."

In certain conformations some of the atoms making up the molecule are more crowded together than in other conformations. Too much crowding between atoms that are not bonded to each other causes them to repel each other. This repulsion raises the energy of the system and makes it less stable. Hence, depending on the molecule, some conformations may have a lower energy

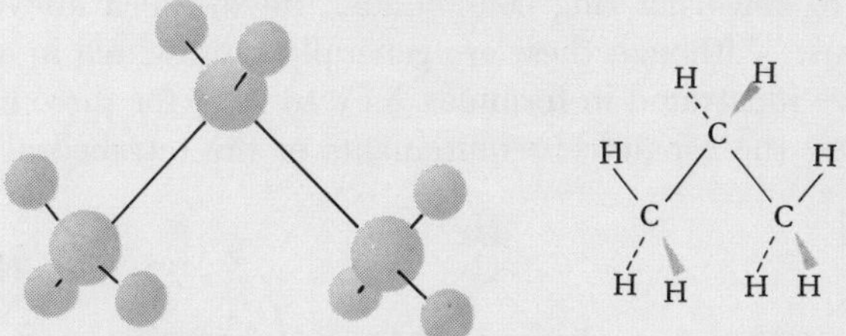

Figure 2–2 Spatial representation of propane. The wedge-shaped bonds indicate that the atom in question points toward the observer, above the plane of the paper. The dotted bonds indicate that the atom in question points away from the observer, below the plane of the paper.

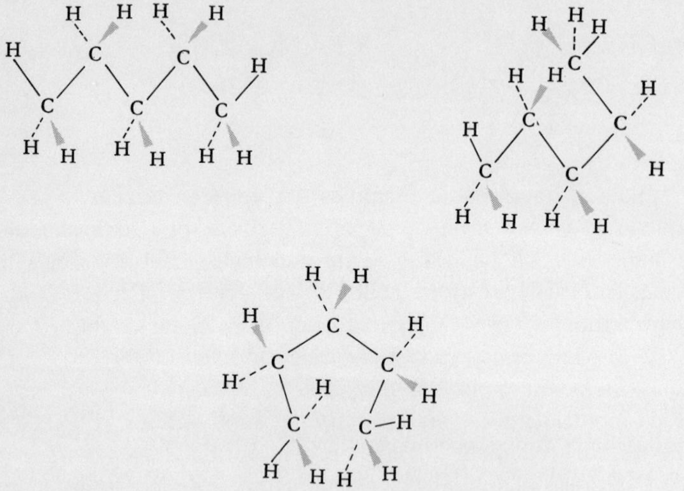

Figure 2–3 Some conformations of *n*-pentane.

than others and would, we might expect, therefore be more likely to exist than others.

2–5 RING COMPOUNDS

Because the carbon chain can be folded in various ways, it is possible to construct ring compounds, the so-called alicyclic hydrocarbons. Although these are generally represented in a planar fashion, as illustrated in formulas XIV to XVI for three common substances, the geometric requirements of the tetrahedral carbon

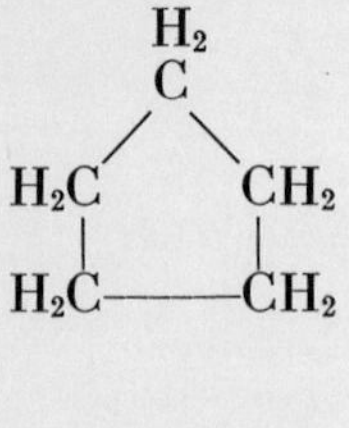

cyclopentane
XIV

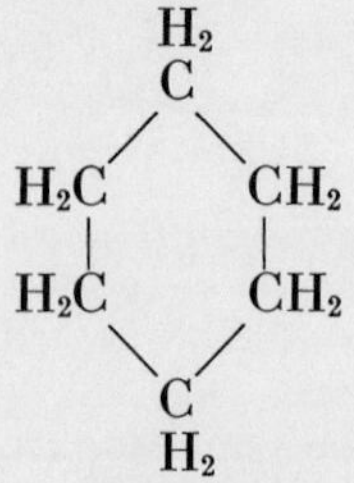

cyclohexane
XV

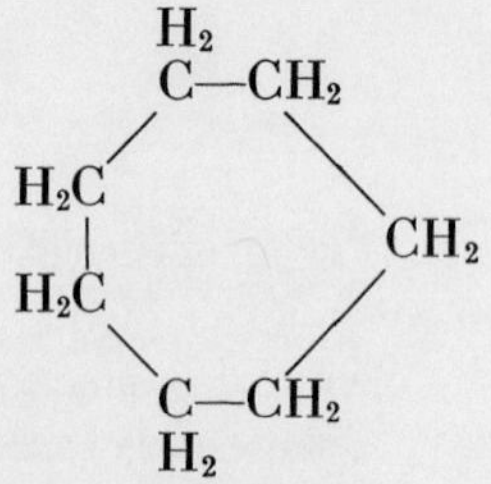

cycloheptane
XVI

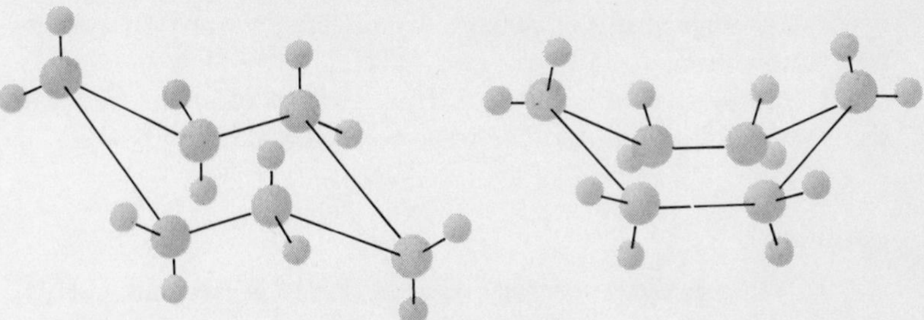

Figure 2–4 Two conformations of cyclohexane.

atom can be met only by a puckering of the rings. This is shown clearly in the ball-and-stick models of cyclohexane (Fig. 2–4).

In a similar way, rings of much larger size can be constructed. On the other hand, it is obviously impossible to construct a three- or four-membered ring without appreciably distorting the tetrahedral angles. In cyclopropane (XVII), for example, the internal angles will have to be 60°, and in cyclobutane (XVIII), 90° compared with a normal angle of 109°28′. These substances are known, but their chemical properties reflect the distortion which we have deduced here.

H_2
C
H_2C 60° CH_2
cyclopropane
XVII

H_2C—CH_2
90°
H_2C—CH_2
cyclobutane
XVIII

2–6 SUMMARY

The structure of an organic molecule is defined as the arrangement in space of the various atoms which are linked to each other by chemical bonds.

Compounds that have the same empirical formulas but different structures are called isomers.

The four bonds that carbon forms with other elements, or indeed with other atoms of carbon, are directed toward the corners of a tetrahedron.

Conformations are different arrangements of atoms that can be converted into one another without the breaking of bonds.

PROBLEMS

1. What is the percentage composition of acetic acid, $C_2H_4O_2$ (see p. 4).

2. The experimentally determined composition of methanol is C, 37.5%; H, 12.5%; O, 50%. Show how this leads to the empirical formula CH_4O given on p. 6.

3. The experimentally determined composition of ethyl alcohol is C, 52.17%; H, 13.04%; O, 34.78%. Show how this leads to the empirical formula C_2H_6O.

4. Why do the facts presented on p. 8 rule out the following structure for methane—a pyramid with a *rectangular* base? (*Hint:* how many isomers could you write for bromomethane if this were so?)

5. Write structural formulas for all isomers of the molecular formula C_6H_{14}. Would it be possible to construct an alicyclic hydrocarbon with this formula?

III

The Shape of Molecules—The Single Bond

At this point it is appropriate to ask: What is the nature of the bonds (the sticks of our models) which hold the atoms of organic molecules together and place them in more or less fixed positions relative to each other? To answer this question in terms of current ideas, a brief review of atomic theory is necessary.

3–1 ORBITALS

The negatively charged electrons that surround the positively charged atomic nucleus are not of equal energy. We have learned to describe their properties by mathematical expressions called wave equations. Solutions to these equations are called wave functions, but precise solutions for atoms other than the hydrogen atom have not yet been found. Even an exact solution does not tell us the exact position of an electron with a particular energy; it permits us only to calculate the probability of finding the electron in a particular place. This solution, or wave function, is called an *orbital*. An orbital is a measure of the region in space where the electron is likely to be found.

For the hydrogen atom, the wave function or orbital of lowest

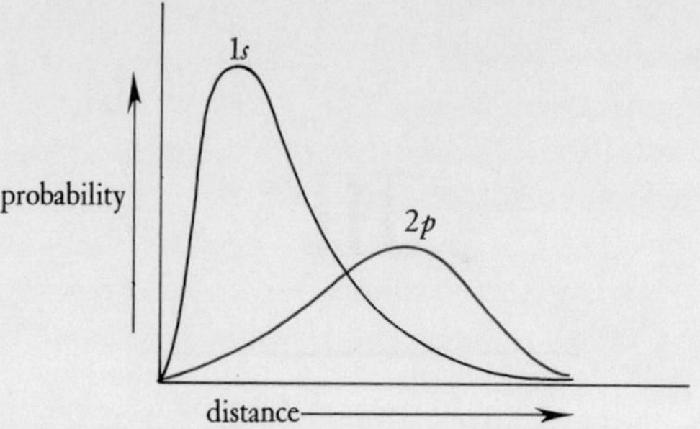

(*a*) probability of finding a 1*s* and a 2*p* electron in
ell of unit thickness around the nucleus

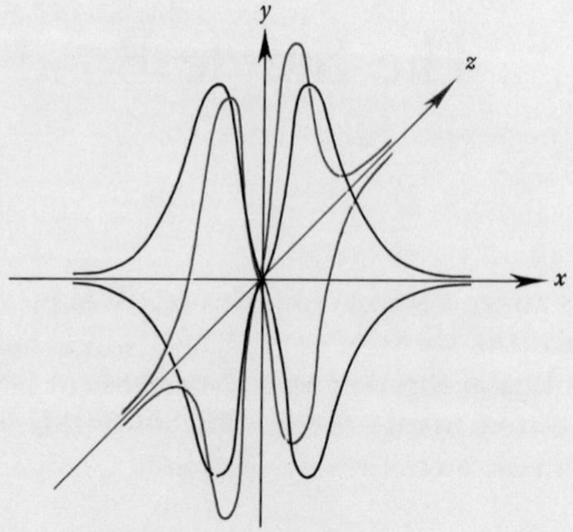

(*b*) three-dimensional probability

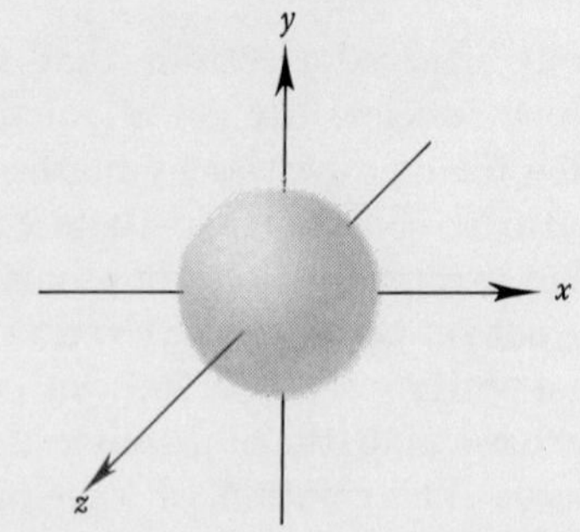

(*c*) 1*s* orbital model

Figure 3–1 Connection between probability curves and orbital model for 1s electrons.

energy is called the 1*s* orbital. Wave functions of higher energy are the 2*s* orbital and three 2*p* orbitals, followed next by a 3*s* orbital and three 3*p* orbitals. The *s* orbitals are spherically symmetrical around the nucleus, as illustrated in Fig. 3–1. The fuzziness of the sphere indicates that the probability of finding an *s* electron in a given shell of unit thickness around the nucleus increases relatively sharply as the distance from the nucleus increases from zero to about 0.5 A and then decreases more slowly, but never vanishes entirely. The approximate shape of a 2*p* orbital is shown in Fig. 3–2. The three 2*p* orbitals are oriented perpendicularly to each other.

Although exact wave functions for atoms containing more than one extranuclear electron have not been found, approximate wave functions similar to those found for the hydrogen atom can be derived to describe the properties of the additional electrons. The energies now increase in the order 1*s*, 2*s*, 2*p*, 3*s*, 3*p*, and so on, where the numerals 1, 2, 3, . . . indicate the principal energy levels or shells of the electrons.

Electrons are assigned to orbitals of lowest energy, but no orbital can be occupied by more than two electrons. Further, an orbital can be occupied by two electrons only if the electrons have opposite *spin*, a property which describes their behavior in a mag-

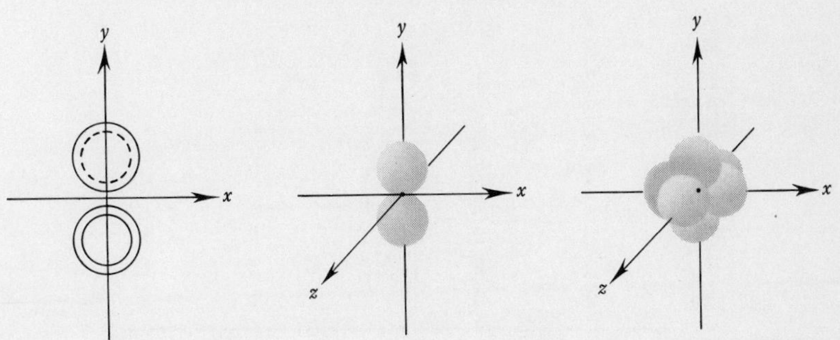

Figure 3–2 Representation of 2*p* orbitals.

netic field.[1] Thus the two extranuclear electrons of helium fill the 1*s* orbital and are said to be paired. Also, if several orbitals of equal energy are available, e.g., the three 2*p* orbitals, none is filled completely until each is occupied by at least one electron.[2]

3–2 THE IONIC BOND

If we apply these rules to the elements of the first two periods, we obtain the electron configurations listed in Table 3–1. The configurations are in harmony with experimental results. It is easier to ionize hydrogen than helium, because the two paired electrons of helium, although approximately as far from the nucleus as the lone electron of hydrogen, are held more tightly by the greater nuclear charge. The unpaired 2*s* electron of lithium, although held by a positive charge of three, is farther away; hence, the energy required to convert lithium to lithium ion, the so-called

Table 3–1
Electron Configuration of the First Ten Elements

	1s	*2s*	*2p*	*2p*	*2p*
H	1				
He	2				
Li	2	1			
Be	2	2			
B	2	2	1		
C	2	2	1	1	
N	2	2	1	1	1
O	2	2	2	1	1
F	2	2	2	2	1
Ne	2	2	2	2	2

[1] This is known as the Pauli exclusion principle, after the physicist who originated the idea.

[2] This is called the Hund rule.

ionization potential[1] of lithium, is less than the ionization potential of hydrogen and also less than that of boron. This leads to the generalization that electronegativity of atoms increases from the left to the right and decreases from the top to the bottom of the periodic table. Elements whose principal energy levels are filled (He, Ne, etc.) exhibit a particular degree of electronic stability and chemical inertness.

The transfer of electrons from the atom of one element with relatively low ionization potential to the atom of another that has great electron affinity may thus produce an over-all energy release and result in the formation of ions. In this manner, complete transfer of the 2*s* electron of lithium to fluorine produces a helium-like structure for lithium ion and a neon-like structure for fluoride ion. The resultant attraction between ions of opposite charge is the ionic bond responsible for the behavior of salts in crystals and in solution.

3–3 THE COVALENT BOND

Many inorganic molecules with which the reader may be familiar are not salt-like. In these, bonds have been formed between two or more atoms which differ not at all or not very much in electronegativity. Examples of molecules in which bonds have been formed between identical atoms are hydrogen and fluorine. Examples of compounds resulting from bond formation between atoms which do not differ very much in electron affinity are water and ammonia. Bonds responsible for the existence of such molecules are called *covalent bonds*.

---

[1] Some definitions may be in order here:

The ionization potential represents the work necessary to remove an electron from a normal atom to an infinite distance in the gaseous state:

$$A \rightarrow A^{+}(\text{ion}) + e^{-}.$$

The electron affinity of an atom is the work required to remove an electron from an ion:

$$A^{-} \rightarrow A + e^{-}.$$

The electronegativity of an atom is the relative power of an atom in a molecule to attract electrons to itself:

$$A{-}B \rightarrow A^{-} + B^{+}.$$

Although the molecules of water, ammonia, and similar compounds are held together by covalent and not ionic bonds, it is interesting to observe that they will orient themselves when placed in an electric field: The more electronegative element will point toward the positive plate and the more electropositive element will point toward the negative plate. This indicates that, although ions are not present, there must be a certain separation of charge, either permanent or induced, which results in a positive and negative "end" of the molecule.

Molecules which orient themselves in an electric field are said to be polar or polarizable, depending on whether or not the separation of charge is permanent. It is difficult to see how polarity of molecules can come about without involving the extranuclear

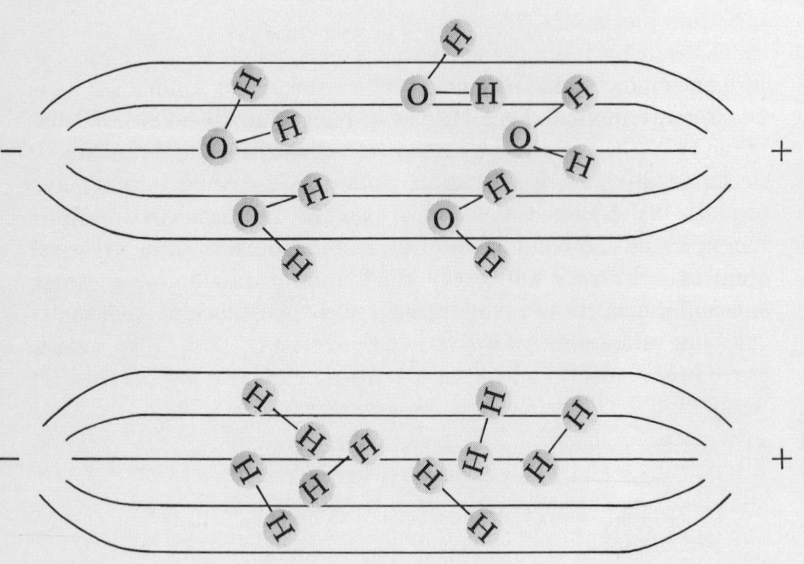

Figure 3–3 Nonpolar and polar molecules in an electric field.

electrons of highest energy, the so-called valence electrons. A gradual transition exists from (1) the purely covalent bond, to be found in nonpolar molecules like hydrogen or fluorine, through (2) ammonia or water to (3) gaseous lithium fluoride, which, although not ionic, is so highly polarized that the transfer of electrons seems essentially complete (Fig. 3–3).

The Hydrogen Molecule

That atoms form molecules through covalent bonds is explained in the following way: It is assumed that the valence electrons can interact with two atomic nuclei simultaneously. In the formation of the hydrogen molecule, for example, the interaction of the two 1*s* electrons with both atomic nuclei must result in the liberation of more energy than is liberated in the interaction of each 1*s* electron with its own hydrogen nucleus. Otherwise, the hydrogen molecule would not be stable. (Before the advent of quantum mechanics this was expressed more simply by the statement that the sharing of the two 1*s* electrons gives each hydrogen atom the more stable helium configuration and therefore results in the liberation of energy.) The properties of the bonding electrons will have to be described by a new wave function which, because it is responsible for the formation of molecules, is called a *molecular orbital.* As in the case of atomic orbitals, each molecular orbital can accommodate only two electrons of opposite spin. If more than two electrons are involved in bonding two or more atoms, molecular orbitals of higher energy must be utilized.

The molecular orbitals may be deduced by adding the atomic wave functions of the bonding electrons. One can picture this in a simple way by allowing the representations of the atomic orbitals to overlap or coalesce. The greater the overlapping of atomic orbitals, the greater is the energy released in forming the bond—the so-called bond strength. Thus in forming the hydrogen molecule one can imagine that the two nuclei are brought together to a distance at which the stabilization produced by the overlapping of the 1*s* orbitals is counterbalanced by the repulsion between the two positively charged nuclei. At this point the distance is 0.74 A and the bond energy is 103 kcal/mole.

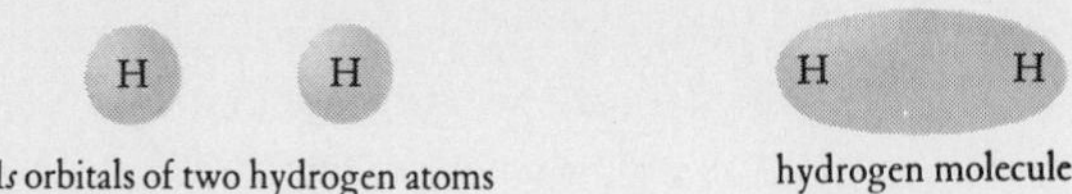

Figure 3–4 Formation of hydrogen molecule from two hydrogen atoms.

The shape of the resulting molecular orbital is illustrated in Fig. 3–4. It is cylindrically symmetrical around the line joining the two atomic nuclei. Such orbitals are called σ orbitals, and the bond formed in this way is called a σ bond.

For the sake of convenience, covalent bonds are generally represented by electron pairs or dashes. The three representations of the hydrogen molecule shown below are entirely equivalent.

The Fluorine Molecule

In a similar way we can rationalize the formation of the fluorine molecule. The electron configuration of fluorine is $1s^2$, $2s^2$, $2p_x^2$, $2p_y^2$, $2p_z^1$, where the superscripts refer to the number of elec-

Figure 3–5 Formation of fluorine molecule from two fluorine atoms.

trons in each orbital. One of the five $2p$ electrons is therefore in a half-full orbital and can interact with a similar $2p$ electron from another fluorine atom as pictured in Fig. 3–5. The two p orbitals overlap, and they change their shape somewhat because most of the electronic charge is concentrated in the area between the two nuclei. The new molecular orbital is cylindrically symmetrical around the line joining the two nuclei, and therefore the fluorine-fluorine bond is a σ bond also.

3–4 THE METHANE MOLECULE

We are now ready to apply these ideas to a consideration of the bonds that exist in the methane molecule and, indeed, in all the hydrocarbons which have been mentioned in the preceding chapter. Methane and the other hydrocarbons are not salt-like. That is to say, they do not ionize in solution, they exhibit low solubility in water and similar solvents, they have low rather than high melting or boiling points, and they are very poor conductors of electricity. Hence the bonds must be covalent rather than ionic.

Inspection of Table 3–1 shows that elemental carbon has two unpaired $2p$ electrons which could presumably interact with unpaired electrons of other atoms. Hence we would expect carbon to form two covalent bonds. But we have seen that carbon has a covalence of four in methane and its relatives, although the existence of compounds in which it has a covalence of two is not impossible.

We could explain a covalence of four by assuming that one of the two paired-$2s$ electrons has been "promoted" to the third, still-vacant $2p$ orbital. This would take some energy, but since carbon could now form four covalent bonds, one involving the lone $2s$ electron and three involving the three unpaired-$2p$ electrons, the extra energy gained in bond formation might more than make up for the promotion energy. Our discussion of the shape of atomic and molecular orbitals indicates that this would lead to three equivalent bonds at right angles to each other and a fourth, different bond exhibiting no particular directional properties.

But we have already deduced that all four bonds emanating from carbon are equivalent and that they are directed to the cor-

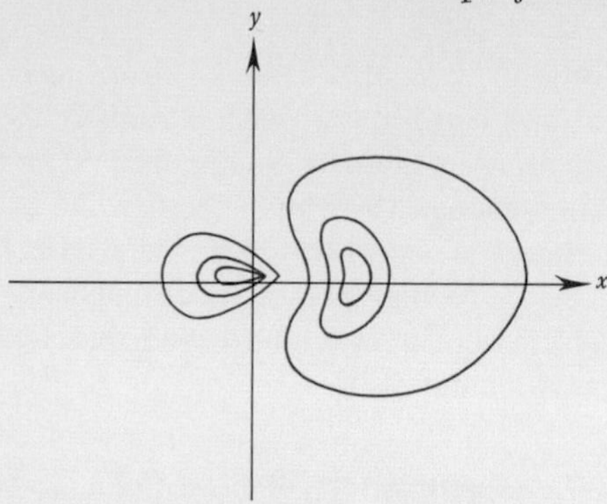

Figure 3–6 Contour lines of a sp^3 hybrid orbital. The sp^3 orbital may be developed from this by rotation about the x axis.

ners of a tetrahedron. Thus the picture of three equivalent bonds at right angles and a fourth, different bond cannot be correct either. Indeed, even theory arrives at the conclusion that more energy will be liberated and the molecule will be more stable if the four bonding orbitals, one s and three p's, are combined to give a new set of four equivalent orbitals, each directed to the corner of a tetrahedron. Such orbitals, formed by the combination of different types of orbitals, are called hybrid orbitals. Since the hybrid orbitals are formed by mixing one $2s$ orbital and three $2p$ orbitals, they are said to be sp^3 hybridized (Fig. 3–6).

In the formation of methane, Fig. 3–7, each of the four sp^3 hybrid orbitals overlaps the $1s$ orbital of a hydrogen atom. The best overlap is obtained if the hydrogen atom lies on the axis of the sp^3 orbital. This results in four molecular orbitals arranged tetrahedrally around the central carbon atom and the tetrahedral distribution of the hydrogens around the carbon. Each of the four molecular orbitals is cylindrically symmetrical around the line joining carbon and hydrogen and therefore constitutes a σ bond. It is important to reemphasize that each of these bonds involves two electrons.

The formation of ethane, Fig. 3–8, similarly involves the union of two CH_3 units in which the four sp^3 hybrid orbitals of each car-

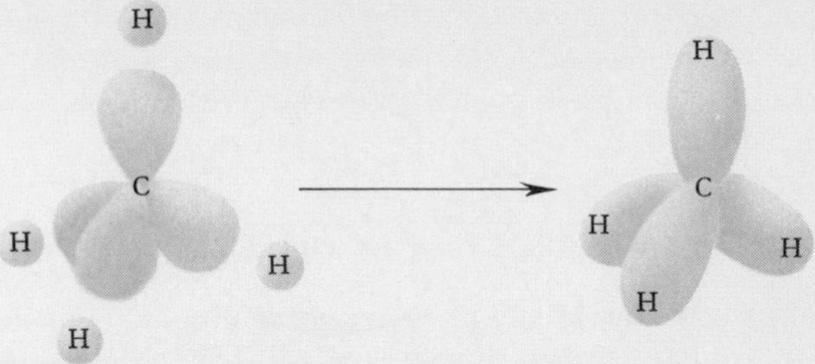

Figure 3–7 Formation of methane from carbon with four sp^3 hybrid orbitals and four hydrogens, each with one 1s orbital.

bon overlap the 1s orbitals of three hydrogen atoms and the vacant sp^3 hybrid orbital of the other carbon.

Carbon and hydrogen have different electronegativities. We might therefore expect that the carbon-hydrogen bond would be somewhat polar, with the electron cloud being slightly displaced toward carbon. This is correct. The molecule as a whole, however, is nonpolar. The tetrahedral shape of the hydrocarbon mole-

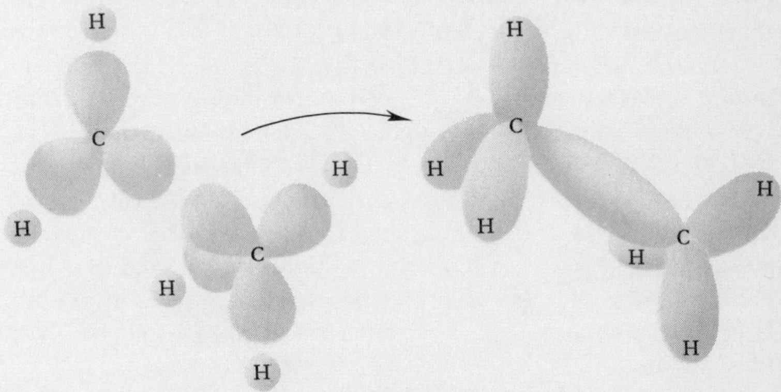

Figure 3–8 Formation of the ethane molecule.

cules has the effect of exactly balancing any such displacement in one bond by the displacements in the three others, so that hydrocarbons as a whole are nonpolar and do not orient themselves in an electric field.

3–5 AMMONIA AND THE AMINES

Let us now look briefly at two other molecules, ammonia and water, as we have looked at methane. Table 3–1 indicates that nitrogen should be trivalent. We would expect that its union with three hydrogen atoms, which results in the formation of the ammonia molecule, would arise from the overlap of its three unpaired $2p$ electrons with the $1s$ electrons of three hydrogen atoms. Hence, the three N—H bonds should be at right angles to each other.

This is not so. Experiment shows that the bond angles are almost exactly those prevailing in a tetrahedral arrangement. This can be explained by assuming that, in ammonia and its derivatives, nitrogen is sp^3 hybridized just as carbon is in methane. One promotes one of the two $2s$ electrons to a p orbital (filling the latter in the process) and combines the $2s$ and $2p$ orbitals as before. Now three of the resulting sp^3 hybrid orbitals are half full and can overlap three $1s$ electrons from hydrogen. The fourth hybrid orbital contains two electrons and is therefore unable to interact with half-filled orbitals from other atoms. The angles are tetrahedral, the unshared electron pair being at the apex, Fig. 3–9.

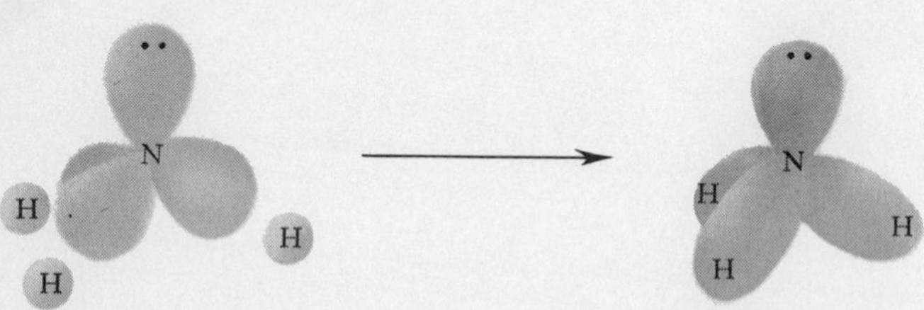

Figure 3–9 Formation of the ammonia molecule from sp^3-hybridized nitrogen.

The three half-filled sp^3 hybrid orbitals of nitrogen can, of course, interact with orbitals of elements other than hydrogen, particularly sp^3 hybrid orbitals of carbon. The result is the class of organic compounds called amines. Depending on the number of hydrogen atoms replaced, one gets primary, secondary, or tertiary amines.

$\ddot{N}(CH_3)(H)(H)$	$\ddot{N}(CH_3)(CH_3)(H)$	$\ddot{N}(CH_3)(CH_3)(CH_3)$
methylamine, a primary amine	dimethylamine, a secondary amine	trimethylamine, a tertiary amine
I	II	III

3–6 WATER, ALCOHOLS, AND ETHERS

In the same way as discussed in the preceding paragraphs, the shape of the water molecule is not what we would expect by consulting Table 3–1, which shows that oxygen could use its two half-filled *p* orbitals to bond with hydrogen. The bond angles are actually 105° instead of the expected 90°. This leads to the proposal that oxygen in water and similar molecules is sp^3 hybridized, two tetrahedron corners being occupied by hydrogen atoms and two by unshared electron pairs, Fig. 3–10. The two half-filled sp^3-

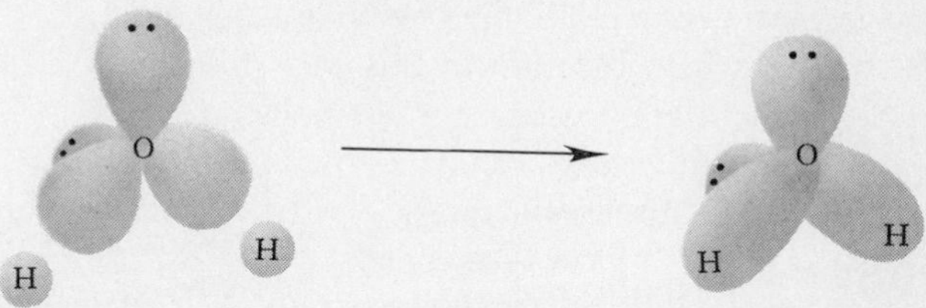

Figure 3–10 Formation of the water molecule from sp^3-hybridized oxygen.

hybridized orbitals may again overlap half-filled orbitals of elements other than hydrogen, such as carbon. In this manner we can explain the shape and behavior of the alcohols and the ethers. The class of ethers includes those organic compounds that may be thought of as having been formed by replacing the two hydrogen atoms of water with organic residues.

CH_3—O—H (O with two lone pairs)

methyl alcohol
IV

CH_3—O—CH_3 (O with two lone pairs)

dimethyl ether
V

3–7 SUMMARY

The properties of extranuclear electrons are described by functions called atomic orbitals.

The extranuclear electrons of separate atoms are responsible for the formation of molecules in two ways:

1. Complete transfer of a valence electron from a less-electronegative to a more-electronegative atom results in the formation of two ions. The attraction between ions of opposite charge is called the ionic bond.

2. Overlap of the atomic orbitals of two electrons belonging to two atoms results in the formation of a molecular orbital containing two electrons. The attraction between the two atoms which results from the formation of a molecular orbital is called a covalent bond.

If the atoms held together in this way differ in electronegativity, the covalent bond is more or less polar.

The shape of molecules held together by covalent bonds is determined by the directional properties of the atomic orbitals which must overlap to form these bonds.

That carbon exhibits a covalence of four and is tetrahedral is explained by assuming that its four valence electrons occupy four sp^3 hybrid orbitals.

PROBLEMS

1. Write electronic structures (using the $1s2s2p$ notation) for the following: the fluoride ion F^-, the beryllium ion Be^{2+}, the aluminum ion Al^{3+}, the sodium ion Na^+, the hydride ion H^-, and the ion Li^-. Can you give a reason why the hydride ion H^- should be encountered frequently, whereas the Li^- ion is not?

2. What shape would you expect the following covalent molecules to have: N_2, BeH_2, BF_3, H_3O^+, H_2S, NH_2^-, and NF_3.

3. The following is an approximate order of electronegativities: $F > O > Cl$ and $N > Br > C > H$. Predict whether the following covalent molecules are polar and, if so, how they will orient themselves in an electric field: HCl, H_2O, CBr_4, methanol, dimethylamine.

IV

The Shape of Molecules—Double and Triple Bonds

IN CHAP. III we discussed theoretical concepts which were developed in order to explain the nature and shape of molecules held together by covalent bonds. Since substances involving the union of carbon atoms constitute the overwhelming preponderance of such molecules, these concepts must accommodate facts dealing not only with the aliphatic hydrocarbons (the alkanes) and their derivatives such as alcohols and amines but also those facts stemming from work with other classes of compounds which have not yet been mentioned.

4-1 ALKENES

One important group of organic substances may be represented by the general formula C_nH_{2n}. These substances are called olefins or alkenes. The simplest stable member of this series is ethylene, C_2H_4, and we are faced with the necessity of developing a representation for it.

Possible Structures of Ethylene

We could assume that ethylene is composed of two different kinds of carbon atom, the first tetravalent and sp^3 hybridized, the second not hybridized and utilizing its two $2p$ orbitals, as illustrated in formula Ia. A second possibility is shown in formula Ib,

Ia Ib

where both carbon atoms are sp^3 hybridized but only two of the four hybrid orbitals of the second carbon atom are filled.

Reactions of Ethylene

At first glance it would appear that either of these formulas is quite satisfactory. Ethylene and its relatives exhibit a much higher degree of chemical reactivity than the alkanes.[1] The reactions involve addition of HBr, HCl, bromine, and many other substances, as indicated in Eqs. (1) to (5).

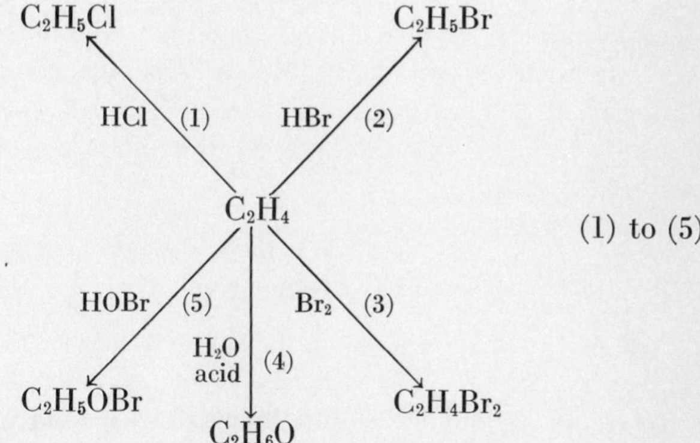

(1) to (5)

[1] In our brief discussion of the alkanes nothing was said about their chemical behavior. Alkanes are remarkably unreactive under "normal" conditions, a fact which accounts for the name "paraffins" (inert substances) frequently applied to them. At high temperatures or in the presence of light, hydrogen can be replaced by halogen, and the alkanes can be oxidized.

Formula Ia might explain this reactivity if we assume that the second carbon atom rehybridizes, thus allowing it to bond to two bromine atoms, one hydrogen and one bromine atom, and so on. Formula Ib already contains two partially vacant atomic orbitals which could be filled by bonding with the reagents listed above. The reaction with hydrogen bromide results in the formation of ethyl bromide, a known compound, and lends substance to this argument:

$$C_2H_4 + HBr \rightarrow \begin{array}{c} \quad H \quad H \\ \quad | \quad\; | \\ H{-}C{-}C{-}Br \\ \quad | \quad\; | \\ \quad H \quad H \end{array} \tag{6}$$

But when we examine the reaction of ethylene with bromine, we find that the two bromine atoms have attached themselves to two different carbon atoms, the product being 1,2-dibromoethane:

$$C_2H_4 + Br_2 \rightarrow \begin{array}{c} \quad H \quad H \\ \quad | \quad\; | \\ H{-}C{-}C{-}H \\ \quad | \quad\; | \\ \quad Br \; Br \end{array} \tag{7}$$

It is logical to assume that the reaction with hydrogen bromide proceeds in the same way. This can be verified by using deuterium bromide:

$$C_2H_4 + DBr \rightarrow \begin{array}{c} \quad H \quad H \\ \quad | \quad\; | \\ H{-}C{-}C{-}H \\ \quad | \quad\; | \\ \quad D \quad Br \end{array} \tag{8}$$

Hence formulas Ia and Ib are incorrect.

Shape of Ethylene

A third possibility would involve sp^3 hybridization of both carbon atoms, each being linked to two hydrogen atoms by σ bonds. One of the two remaining hybrid orbitals would be used up by a carbon-carbon bond, and the other would remain half full as in IIa. Or both of the two unused sp^3 hybrid orbitals could interact with each other, thereby producing what might be called a double bond, IIb. Structures of this type would explain the chemical behavior of the alkenes if the double bond were broken relatively easily.

IIa IIb

Now although the linkage between the two carbon atoms of ethylene is generally referred to as a double bond, experiments show that the bond angles in ethylene and its derivatives are not tetrahedral, or 109°28′, but approximately 120°. In other words, ethylene is a planar molecule and might be represented as in Fig. 4–1*a*. This is considered to rule out formula IIb. Formula IIa is eliminated for this and other reasons. Instead, it is assumed that the carbon atoms make use of three equivalent sp^2 hybrid orbitals which are formed by mixing one atomic *s* and two atomic *p* orbitals. One *p* orbital is left over. We shall discuss what happens to it in the next paragraph. The three sp^2 hybrid orbitals lie in one plane at angles of 120°. Overlap with the 1*s* orbitals of two hydrogens and with another sp^2-hybridized carbon atom produces the shape of Fig. 4–1*b*.

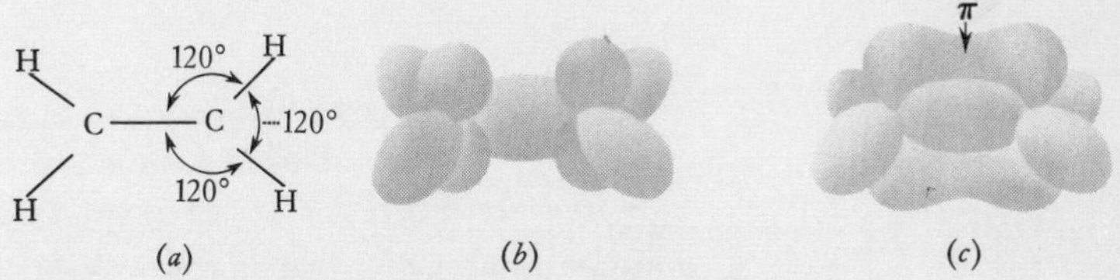

Figure 4–1 The ethylene molecule.

4–2 THE π BOND

In becoming sp^2 hybridized to form the ethylene molecule, each carbon atom retains one p orbital that contains a single electron and lies above and below the plane of the three sp^2 hybrid orbitals. Since the axes of the p orbitals are parallel and the carbon atoms are relatively close, the p orbitals can overlap to some extent. This produces a new kind of molecular orbital whose shape is shown in Fig. 4–1*c*: two sausage-like lobes above and below the line joining the two nuclei. The electrons in this new type of molecular orbital are called π electrons, and the bond formed in this manner is called a π bond.

It should be pointed out that the π bond is formed by two p orbitals overlapping laterally, whereas σ bonds are formed by overlap of atomic orbitals along the bond axis. Now, calculations show that lateral overlap between the two p orbitals is not as good as overlap between the sp^2 hybrid orbitals. The poorer the overlap, the less the energy released and the weaker the bond. This is in accord with the experimental facts. Thus, our brief discussion of the chemical behavior of alkenes indicates that the π bond is broken relatively easily, giving rise to two σ bonds in the process. Furthermore, thermochemical measurements show that the bond strength of the ethylenic "double" bond is not twice the strength of the carbon-carbon single bond of ethane, but somewhat smaller. Nevertheless, in spite of the difference in type and strength between the π bond and the σ bond, the conventional representation of Fig. 4–2 does not distinguish between them.

Figure 4–2 Conventional representation of ethylene; the curved lines in the ball-and-stick model indicate π bonds.

4-3 STRUCTURAL ISOMERISM OF ALKENES

As in all series of organic molecules, other alkenes may be thought of as having been formed from ethylene by linking one or both of the sp^2-hybridized carbon atoms to groups containing carbon. Substances like propylene, 1-butene, and isobutylene are typical, low-molecular-weight alkenes. We note that 1-butene and isobutylene are isomers; they have the same empirical formula C_4H_8, but the carbon skeleton is different. We can easily verify

$$\underset{\substack{\text{propylene}\\ \text{III}}}{CH_3CH{=}CH_2} \qquad \underset{\substack{\text{1-butene}\\ \text{IV}}}{CH_3CH_2CH{=}CH_2} \qquad \underset{\substack{\text{isobutylene}\\ \text{V}}}{CH_3\overset{\overset{CH_3}{|}}{C}{=}CH_2}$$

this by carrying out conversions which are characteristic of the way organic chemists operate:

$$CH_3CH_2CH{=}CH_2 \begin{cases} \xrightarrow[\text{(reduction)}]{H_2\ \text{Pd catalyst}} \underset{n\text{-butane}}{CH_3CH_2CH_2CH_3} \\ \xrightarrow{\text{oxidation}} \underset{\text{formic acid}}{HCO_2H} + \underset{\text{propionic acid}}{CH_3CH_2CO_2H} \end{cases} \tag{9}$$

$$CH_3\overset{\overset{CH_3}{|}}{C}{=}CH_2 \begin{cases} \xrightarrow[\text{(reduction)}]{H_2,\ \text{Pd catalyst}} \underset{\text{2-methyl-propane}}{CH_3\overset{\overset{CH_3}{|}}{C}CH_3} \\ \xrightarrow{\text{oxidation}} \underset{\text{formic acid}}{HCO_2H} + \underset{\text{acetone}}{CH_3COCH_3} \end{cases} \tag{10}$$

Thus, hydrogen can be added to alkenes in the presence of catalysts. This breaks the π bond and results in the formation of alkanes, whose isolation gives a clue to the nature of the starting material. Alternatively, oxidation of the alkene with potassium permanganate or ozone, a treatment which has no effect on alkanes, breaks the carbon chain at the position of the ethylenic bond and gives characteristic fragments from which the nature of the starting material can be pieced together. Equation (9) illustrates this procedure for 1-butene; Eq. (10), for isobutylene.

One would predict the existence of a third alkene isomer of formula C_4H_8, 2-butene, whose catalytic hydrogenation should result in *n*-butane and whose oxidation should yield two molecules of acetic acid:

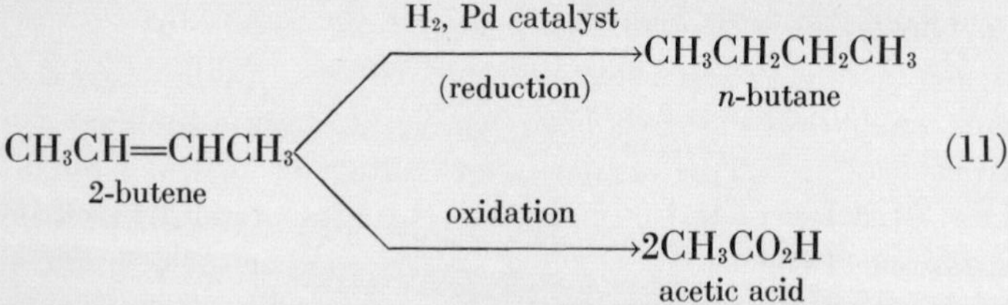

(11)

In fact, two such substances have been found. Their physical properties are clearly different, but hydrogenation transforms both of them to *n*-butane and oxidation transforms them to acetic acid. Hence, there must be two isomers of 2-butene which differ not in double-bond position but in some other way (Fig. 4–3). How can this be explained?

cis-2-butene

trans-2-butene

Figure 4–3 Two isomers of 2-butene.

4–4 GEOMETRIC ISOMERISM OF ALKENES

The conventional representation of 2-butene clearly shows that two models which differ from each other in the spatial relationships of the carbon atoms can be constructed. These models are not interconvertible unless one of the bonds linking the central carbon atoms is broken. In terms of the picture which we have developed for the ethylene molecule, the two p orbitals of the central, sp^2-hybridized carbon atoms overlap best if they are parallel to each other. This results in the formation of the π bond. To pass from one of the 2-butenes to the other requires twisting, or rotation, of the central bond in such a way that the p orbitals no longer overlap and the π bond is broken (see Fig. 4–4). This takes more energy than is normally available. As a consequence, restricted rotation around the double bond at the temperatures ordinarily employed by the organic chemist is the rule.

The consequence of this restricted rotation about double bonds is the phenomenon called *geometric isomerism.* The two butenes are said to be "geometric" isomers and to differ from each other in configuration. To denote the configuration, the prefixes *cis* (meaning "on the same side") and *trans* ("on opposite sides") are used. Geometric isomerism of the 2-butene type is possible in all alkenes whose ethylenic carbon atoms carry two different groups. Figure 4–5 illustrates the use of the terms *cis* and *trans* when three or more different groups are attached to the carbons linked by the double bond.

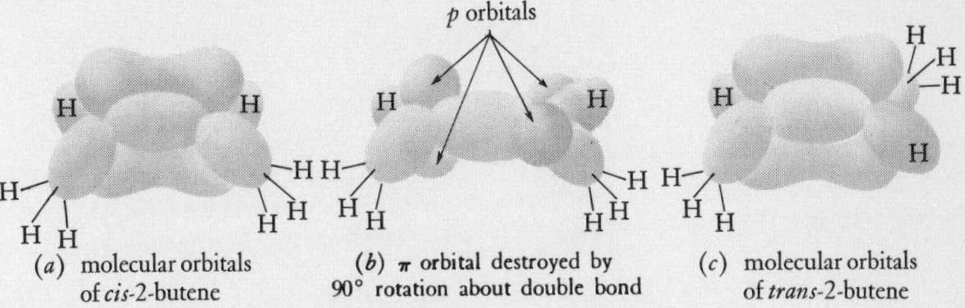

Figure 4–4 Rotation about double bonds.

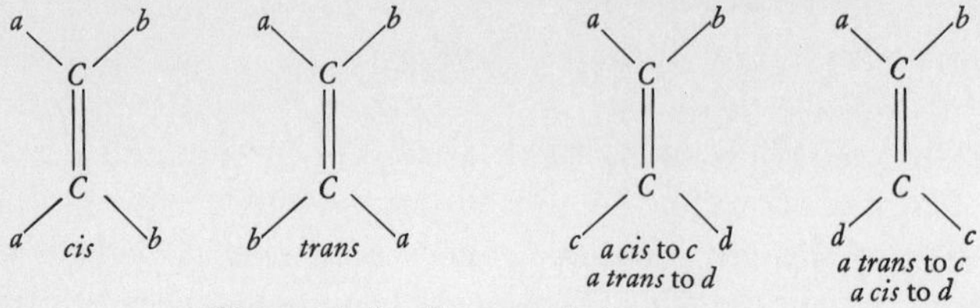

cis *trans* *a cis* to *c*, *a trans* to *d* *a trans* to *c*, *a cis* to *d*

Figure 4–5 Geometric isomers.

4–5 RESTRICTED ROTATION

Organic chemists have wondered whether restricted rotation about single bonds might not, in certain cases, lead to the existence of isomers. Their reasoning is as follows.

Normal butane could be represented by the projection formula I, Fig. 4–6, in which one looks "along" the central carbon-carbon bond. The nearer carbon atom with its three substituents (two hydrogen atoms and one methyl group) is denoted by the inverted Y; the more distant carbon atom with its substituents (also two hydrogen atoms and one CH_3— group) by the circle. As the carbon atoms rotate around the central bond, the molecule will first assume conformation II, in which all six substituents are said to be eclipsed. Eclipsed conformations are less stable than conformations I, III, and IV, which are said to be staggered, because of repulsive forces that come into play when atoms approach each other closely (see p. 11). However, most open-chain molecules

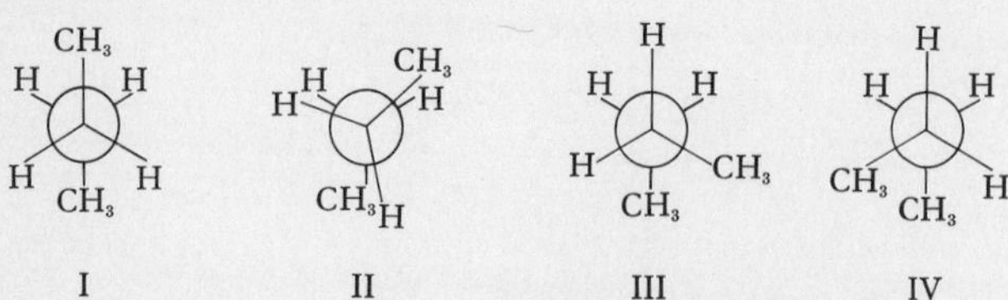

Figure 4–6 Conformations of *n*-butane.

have enough energy to pass from conformation I to III and IV through eclipsed conformations of type II. Conformations III and IV are equivalent, but they are assumed to be less stable than conformation I because in I the two CH_3— groups are as far from each other as possible.

Now one could imagine certain molecules in which the substituents are very bulky. The energy of the eclipsed conformations might then be so high that conformations of type I could not convert readily to conformations of type III at room temperature. While this has not been observed in open-chain molecules, the application of the principle to some other compounds has shown that under certain circumstances restricted rotation around single bonds is possible.

4–6 GEOMETRIC ISOMERISM IN RING COMPOUNDS

The existence of geometric isomers may also be demonstrated in ring compounds, where the near and the more distant carbon atoms are connected with each other directly *and* through a chain of carbon atoms. This is illustrated diagrammatically in Fig. 4–7 for cyclohexane, where we are again looking along the central carbon-carbon bond. The loop containing the assemblage —$(CH_2)_4$— represents the remaining parts of the ring compound. Conformation I can be converted to conformation II without undue strain by rotating the more distant carbon atom through an angle of 120°. Similarly, by rotating the rear carbon atom of III through an angle of 120°, we obtain IV. However, no simple rotation will permit the conversion of either I to III or II to IV. It is

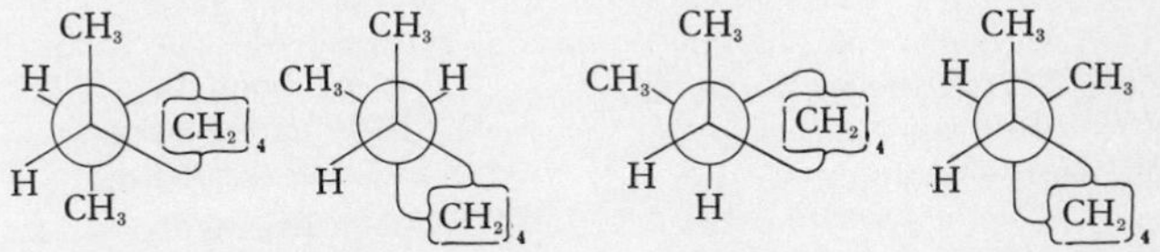

I II III IV

Figure 4–7 Conformations of 1,2-dimethylcyclohexane.

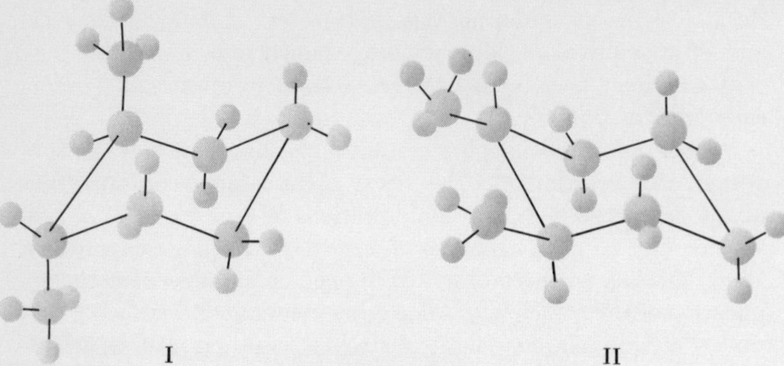

Figure 4–8 Two conformations of *trans*-1,2-dimethylcyclohexane.

impossible to carry out these transformations without breaking a carbon-carbon bond. A molecule of this sort should therefore exist in two geometric forms, I or II, the *trans* isomer, and III or IV, the *cis* isomer.[1]

Ball-and-stick models of the *trans* isomer of 1,2-dimethylcyclohexane (chair conformation) are illustrated in Fig. 4–8. I and II are related in the same way as are I and II of Fig. 4–7. The *cis* isomer of 1,2-dimethylcyclohexane is depicted in Fig. 4–9, where III and IV correspond to III and IV of Fig. 4–7. These two compounds have been known for a long time, but the exact shape of

[1] The names "cis" and "trans" are applied to these compounds in the same way as they were to the alkenes (p. 37). The reader may see this easily in I of Figs. 4–7 and 4–8, which represents a conformation of *trans*-1,2-dimethylcyclohexane. The methyl groups are "on opposite sides" of the ring. However, the reader may become somewhat confused when he looks at conformation II. Although this represents the same compound, *trans*-1,2-dimethylcyclohexane, the methyl groups seem to be "on the same side."

The difficulty arises because the cyclohexane ring is puckered and not planar. The nomenclature, however, is based on the arrangement of the two methyl groups in a hypothetical planar ring.

The relative disposition of the two methyl groups in both conformations of the cis isomer (III and IV) stays the same.

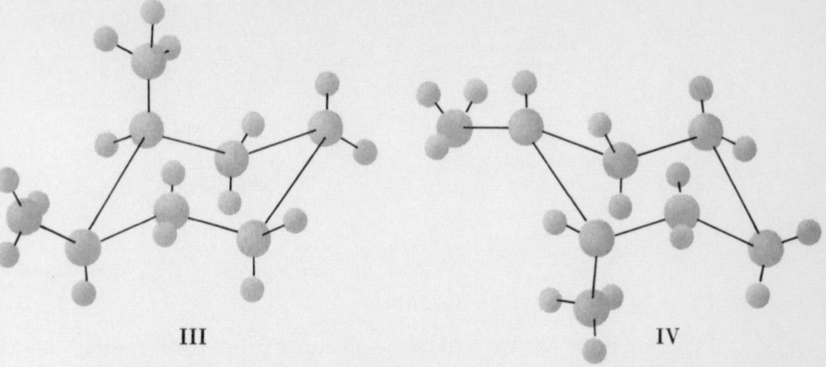

Figure 4–9 Two conformations of *cis*-1,2-dimethylcyclohexane.

such molecules has not been a matter of much interest until recently.

4–7 CARBONYL COMPOUNDS

Trigonally hybridized carbon is found not only in alkenes but in other types of compound as well. The most important of these contain the so-called carbonyl group, which is conventionally represented as $\rangle C{=}O$. Depending on whether the carbon atom is attached to one hydrogen and an organic residue, two organic groups, or one organic group and one —OH, we speak of aldehydes, ketones, or carboxylic acids. Other, similar substances containing a carbonyl group are also listed below.

$CH_3C(=O)H$	$(CH_3)_2C{=}O$	$CH_3C(=O)OH$
acetaldehyde, an aldehyde	acetone, a ketone	acetic acid, a carboxylic acid
VI	VII	VIII

$$\underset{\substack{\text{ethyl acetate,}\\ \text{an ester}\\ \text{IX}}}{CH_3C(=O)OCH_2CH_3} \qquad \underset{\substack{\text{acetamide,}\\ \text{an amide}\\ \text{X}}}{CH_3C(=O)NH_2}$$

Reactions of Carbonyl Compounds

The reactions of the carbonyl group are generally those of addition, as was also typical of alkenes. Equations (12) and (13) illustrate the addition of hydrogen to the carbonyl group of acetaldehyde and the addition of hydrogen cyanide to the carbonyl group of acetone:

$$CH_3C(=O)H + H_2 \xrightarrow{\text{catalyst}} CH_3CH_2OH \qquad (12)$$

$$CH_3\underset{\underset{O}{\|}}{C}CH_3 + HCN \rightleftarrows CH_3\overset{\overset{OH}{|}}{\underset{\underset{CN}{|}}{C}}{-}CH_3 \qquad (13)$$

The occurrence of addition reactions indicates the presence of a bond which can be broken relatively easily—more easily, in fact,

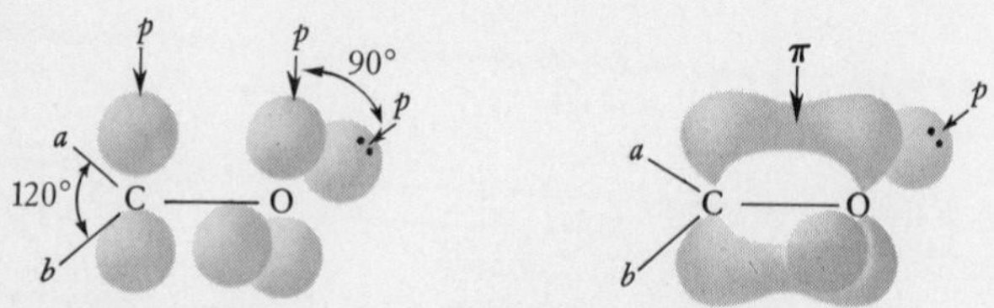

Figure 4–10 The carbonyl group.

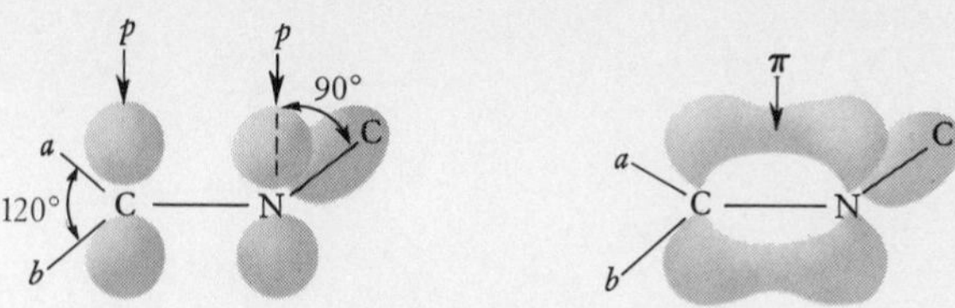

Figure 4–11 The C≡N group.

than the regular carbon-carbon bond—and which is somewhat comparable in strength to the π bond of alkenes. Since the bond angles of the carbonyl carbon are approximately 120°, a simple picture of the carbonyl carbon suggests that it is sp^2 hybridized and linked to three other groups, one of which is oxygen, by three σ bonds (Fig. 4–10). We recall that the electronic structure of oxygen is $1s^2 2s^2 2p_x^2 2p_y^1 2p_z^1$. The remaining p orbital of carbon overlaps the other half-filled p orbital of oxygen and thus forms a π bond. This would result in a molecule which is flat in the vicinity of the carbonyl group. In a similar way, carbon can be linked to nitrogen (Fig. 4–11).

The reader will recall that we have assumed that oxygen is sp^3 hybridized in water, alcohols, and ether. To explain the properties of the carbonyl group, it is also possible to assume that oxygen, like carbon, is sp^2 hybridized. This leads to the diagrams in Fig. 4–12. In the same way the nitrogen of the —C═N group may be sp^2 hybridized (see Fig. 4–13).

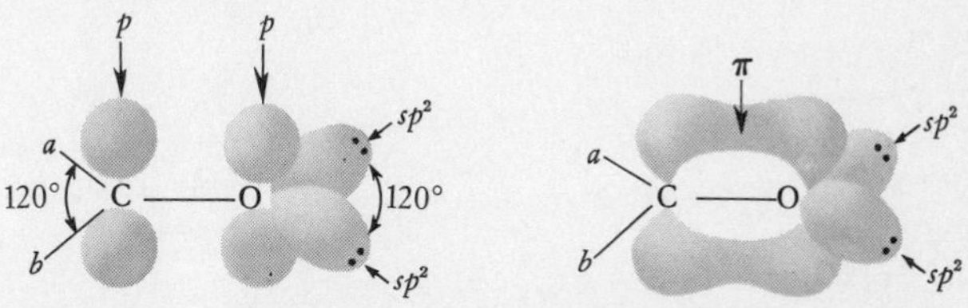

Figure 4–12 The C═O group (oxygen sp^2 hybridized).

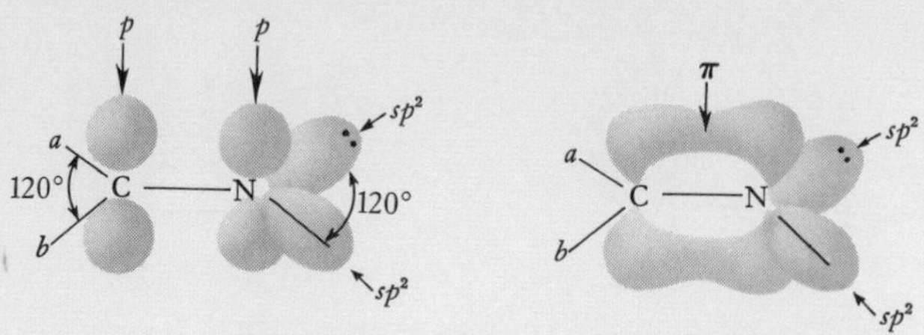

Figure 4–13 The C≡N group (nitrogen sp^2 hybridized).

4–8 ACETYLENES

To complete the picture, we must discuss one additional type of hydrocarbon which has not previously been mentioned. The class of acetylenes, or alkynes, is represented by the general formula C_nH_{2n-2}.

The reactions of acetylene indicate that each of the carbon atoms is associated with one hydrogen atom. For example, addition of bromine, Eq. (14), results first in the formation of sym-

$$C_2H_2 \xrightarrow{Br_2} \underset{\text{sym. dibromo-ethylene}}{CHBr{=}CHBr} \xrightarrow{Br_2} \underset{\text{1,1,2,2-tetrabromo-ethane}}{CHBr_2CHBr_2} \tag{14}$$

metrical 1,2-dibromoethylene and then in 1,1,2,2-tetrabromoethane. Hydrogen chloride adds as indicated in Eq. (15). The

$$C_2H_2 \xrightarrow{HCl} \underset{\text{vinyl chloride}}{CH_2{=}CHCl} \xrightarrow{HCl} \underset{\text{1,1-dichloroethane}}{CH_3CHCl_2} \tag{15}$$

initial product is vinyl chloride (or chloroethylene); the final product is 1,1-dichloroethane.

4–9 THE TRIPLE BOND

The initial reaction of Eq. (14) causes the formation of halogen derivatives of an alkene with whose structure we are familiar. Two new σ bonds between carbon and bromine have been formed. It is

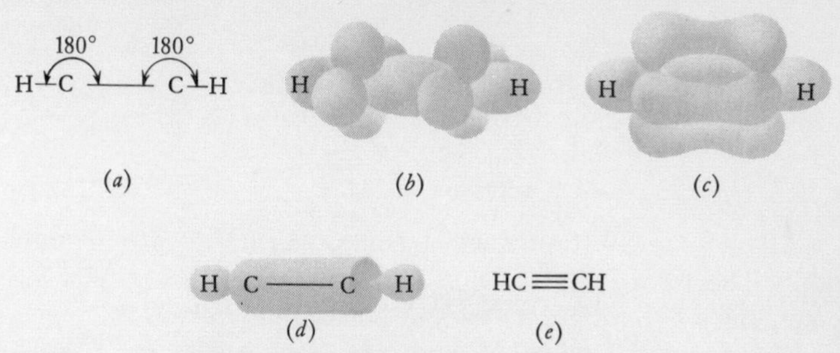

Figure 4–14 The acetylene molecule.

therefore logical to assume that the two carbon atoms of acetylene are linked by one σ and two π bonds, just as the carbon atoms of ethylene are linked by one σ and one π bond. The carbon atoms are said to be *sp* hybridized, a type of hybridization which comes about by mixing one atomic *s* and one atomic *p* orbital. The two new orbitals are called *sp* orbitals; the angle between them is 180°. One *sp* orbital overlaps the 1*s* orbital of hydrogen; the other, the half-full *sp* orbital of a similarly hybridized carbon atom. Hence, the shape of acetylene is linear, Fig. 4–14.

Each carbon atom has used only one of its three 2*p* orbitals to form the *sp* hybrid orbitals. The remaining *p* orbitals, each occupied by one electron, are at right angles to each other and to the molecular orbital formed by the *sp* hybrids, as shown in Fig. 4–14*b*. Overlapping of *p* orbitals from the adjoining carbon atoms results in the two π bonds shown in Fig. 4–14*c*. However, this picture does not accurately represent the electron distribution in acetylene. The two π bonds interact with each other, so that the electron distribution is cylindrically symmetrical around the line joining the carbon atoms, as in 4–14*d*. The bond formed in this way, customarily called a triple bond, is represented as in Fig. 4–14*e*.

It is apparent that the linearity of the acetylene molecule will not permit the existence of geometrical isomers even if the hydrogen atoms are substituted by various groups.

Carbon-oxygen triple bonds are rare and will not be considered here. On the other hand, the electron configuration of nitrogen permits the existence of many stable compounds of the type shown below. They are called nitriles or cyanides.

$$CH_3C{\equiv}N \quad \text{or} \quad CH_3CN$$

acetonitrile, an organic cyanide

XI

4–10 SUMMARY

Alkenes are substances which contain a carbon-carbon double bond. The term "double bond" is actually somewhat of a misnomer, since two different types of bond are involved.

The carbons involved in double-bond formation are assumed to be sp^2 hybridized. The first of the two bonds is formed by the overlap of two sp^2 hybrid orbitals, one from each carbon. The second bond is formed by the overlap of two p orbitals, one from each carbon.

The directional properties of sp^2 hybrid orbitals determine the shape of alkenes. Restricted rotation about double bonds gives rise to geometric isomerism. Restricted rotation about single bonds is also possible; it is responsible for the existence of molecules in different conformations.

Substances containing carbon-oxygen double bonds are said to contain the carbonyl group.

Alkynes are substances which contain a carbon-carbon triple bond. The carbons involved in triple-bond formation are assumed to be sp hybridized. The first of the three bonds is formed by the overlap of two sp hybrid orbitals, one from each carbon. The other two bonds are formed by the overlap of four p orbitals, two from each carbon.

PROBLEMS

1. Draw structures of the six different isomeric alkenes that have the empirical formula C_5H_{10}. How many pairs of geometric isomers are included among the six?

2. Consider the two substances shown below:

```
CH3CH2         CH2CH3        CH3CH2          H
      \       /                    \       /
       C==C                          C==C
      /       \                    /       \
     H         H                  H         CH2CH3
```

cis-3-hexene *trans*-3-hexene

In which way will they differ from each other: (a) boiling point, (b) product of hydrogenation, (c) solubility in diethyl ether (d) products of oxidation, or (e) density

3. State whether the following substances can exist as *cis-trans* isomer pairs

$CH_2{=}CCl_2$ $CHCl{=}CHCl$

$CH_2{=}CFBr$ $CH_3C{\equiv}CCH_3$

4. Write equations for the following reactions:
addition of hydrogen to propylene
addition of hydrogen cyanide to

$$CH_3{-}CH_2{-}C\overset{\displaystyle O}{\underset{\displaystyle H}{\lessgtr}}$$

(propionaldehyde)

addition of bromine to $CH_3C{\equiv}CCH_3$ (2-butyne)
oxidation of $CH_2{=}CHCH_2CH_2CH_3$ (1-pentene)

V

Making and Breaking Bonds

IN TRYING TO DEVELOP PLAUSIBLE IDEAS about the structure of alkanes, alkenes, alkynes, and some of their simple relatives, we have had to rely heavily on the facts which emerged from a study of the reactions of the compounds.

5-1 REACTIONS OF ALKANES

To recapitulate, alkanes are generally inert, although high-temperature reactions may result in replacement, or substitution, of hydrogen by halogen, in removal of hydrogen, or in breaking of the carbon chain. This is illustrated in Eqs. (1) to (3) for propane; other alkanes behave analogously.

Chlorination

$$CH_3CH_2CH_3 + Cl_2 \xrightarrow[\text{temperature}]{\text{light or high}} \underset{\substack{\text{1-chloropropane} \\ (n\text{-propyl} \\ \text{chloride})}}{CH_3CH_2CH_2Cl} + \underset{\substack{\text{2-chloropropane} \\ \text{(isopropyl} \\ \text{chloride)}}}{\underset{\displaystyle Cl}{\underset{|}{CH_3CHCH_3}}} \qquad (1)$$

Dehydrogenation

$$CH_3CH_2CH_3 \xrightarrow[\text{catalyst}]{\text{high temperature}} CH_3CH{=}CH_2 + H_2 \qquad (2)$$

Cracking

$$CH_3CH_2CH_3 \xrightarrow[\text{catalyst}]{\text{high temperature}} CH_2{=}CH_2 + CH_4 \qquad (3)$$

The initial products of halogenation may be treated with more halogen until most, if not all, of the hydrogen atoms have been replaced. This is an example of a substitution reaction.

5-2 ADDITION REACTIONS OF ALKENES AND ALKYNES

The alkenes and the alkynes, on the other hand, are highly reactive; they undergo what are called addition reactions. Some of the most important ones are shown in Eqs. (4) to (7), with isobutylene and 1-butyne serving as examples.

Hydrogenation

$$CH_3\overset{\overset{CH_3}{|}}{C}{=}CH_2 + H_2 \xrightarrow{\text{Pd}} \underset{\text{isobutane}}{CH_3\overset{\overset{CH_3}{|}}{C}HCH_3} \qquad (4)$$

$$CH_3CH_2C{\equiv}CH + H_2 \xrightarrow{\text{Pd}}$$

$$\underset{\text{1-butene}}{CH_3CH_2CH{=}CH_2} \xrightarrow[H_2]{\text{Pd}} \underset{n\text{-butane}}{CH_3CH_2CH_2CH_3} \qquad (5)$$

Halogenation

$$CH_3\overset{\overset{CH_3}{|}}{C}{=}CH_2 + Br_2 \xrightarrow[CCl_4]{\text{solvent}} \underset{\text{2-methyl-1,2-dibromobutane}}{CH_3\overset{\overset{CH_3}{|}}{\underset{\underset{Br}{|}}{C}}CH_2Br} \qquad (6)$$

$$CH_3CH_2C{\equiv}CH + Br_2 \rightarrow$$

$$\underset{\text{1,2-dibromo-1-butene}}{CH_3CH_2\underset{\underset{Br}{|}}{C}{=}CHBr} \xrightarrow{Br_2} \underset{\text{1,1,2,2-tetrabromobutane}}{CH_3CH_2\overset{\overset{Br}{|}}{\underset{\underset{Br}{|}}{C}}CHBr_2} \qquad (7)$$

Hydrohalogenation

$$CH_3\overset{\overset{\displaystyle CH_3}{|}}{C}{=}CH_2 + HCl \rightarrow CH_3\underset{\underset{\displaystyle Cl}{|}}{\overset{\overset{\displaystyle CH_3}{|}}{C}}CH_3 \qquad (8)$$

tert-butyl chloride

$$CH_3CH_2C{\equiv}CH + HCl \rightarrow$$

$$CH_3CH_2\underset{\underset{\displaystyle Cl}{|}}{C}{=}CH_2 \xrightarrow{HCl} CH_3CH_2\underset{\underset{\displaystyle Cl}{|}}{\overset{\overset{\displaystyle Cl}{|}}{C}}CH_3 \qquad (9)$$

2-chloro-1-butene 2,2-dichlorobutane

Hydration

$$CH_3\overset{\overset{\displaystyle CH_3}{|}}{C}{=}CH_2 + H_2O \xrightarrow{H_2SO_4} CH_3\underset{\underset{\displaystyle OH}{|}}{\overset{\overset{\displaystyle CH_3}{|}}{C}}CH_3 \qquad (10)$$

tert-butyl alcohol

$$CH_3CH_2C{\equiv}CH + H_2O \xrightarrow[HgSO_4]{H_2SO_4}$$

$$CH_3CH_2\underset{\underset{\displaystyle OH}{|}}{C}{=}CH_2 \rightleftharpoons CH_3CH_2\underset{\underset{\displaystyle O}{\|}}{C}CH_3 \qquad (11)$$

2-butanone, a ketone[1]

Addition of Unsymmetrical Reagents

When we look at the hydrohalogenation and hydration reactions, some interesting facts emerge. Isobutylene is an unsym-

[1] The initial product, 2-hydroxy-1-butene, is in equilibrium with the isomeric and more stable substance 2-butanone. This phenomenon is known as *tautomerism* and the two substances are referred to as *tautomers*.

metrical alkene, and 1-butyne is an unsymmetrical alkyne. In these substances, the two carbon atoms linked by a double or triple bond are not substituted equally. Now, the addition of an unsymmetrical reagent like hydrogen chloride to isobutylene could theoretically take place in two different ways, giving 1-chloro-2-methylpropane or *tert*-butyl chloride, Eq. (12). Yet only *tert*-butyl

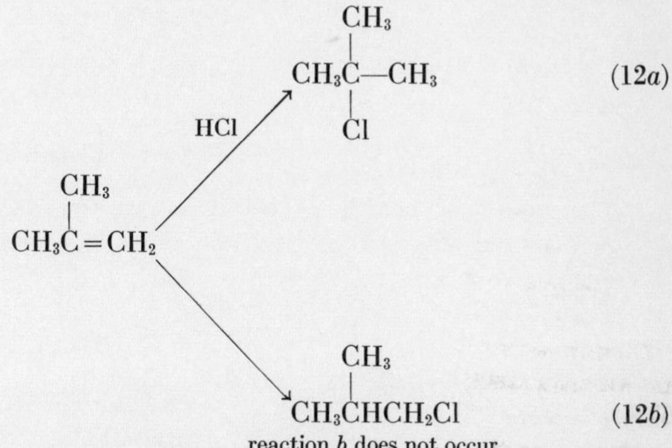

reaction *b* does not occur

chloride is formed. Similarly, addition of hydrogen chloride to 1-butyne results first in the formation of 2-chloro-1-butene and later in 2,2-dichlorobutane; no isomers can be detected. Again, only one substance, *tert*-butyl alcohol, is formed when isobutylene is treated with dilute sulfuric acid; and 1-butyne behaves similarly. In fact, all reactions of this type involve addition of hydrogen to that carbon which already carries more hydrogen atoms. The halide or hydroxyl group adds to that carbon which carries the lesser number of hydrogen atoms.

5–3 OXIDATION OF ALKENES

The characteristic oxidation reactions of alkenes involve, in a manner of speaking, addition of oxygen or oxygen-containing groups to the double bond. Treatment with potassium permanganate, Eqs. (13) and (14), cleaves the carbon chain and produces two fragments whose nature is characteristic of the starting material:

$$\mathrm{CH_3\overset{\displaystyle CH_3}{\overset{|}{C}}{=}CHCH_3 + KMnO_4 \xrightarrow{\text{dilute aqueous}} CH_3\overset{\displaystyle CH_3}{\overset{|}{\underset{\underset{\displaystyle OH}{|}}{C}}}{-}\underset{\underset{\displaystyle OH}{|}}{C}HCH_3} \qquad (13)$$

2-methyl-2-butene — 2-methyl-2,3-butanediol, a glycol

$$\mathrm{CH_3\overset{\displaystyle CH_3}{\overset{|}{\underset{\underset{\displaystyle OH}{|}}{C}}}{-}\underset{\underset{\displaystyle OH}{|}}{C}CH_3 + KMnO_4 \rightarrow CH_3\underset{\underset{\displaystyle O}{\|}}{C}CH_3 + CH_3CO_2H} \qquad (14)$$

acetone — acetic acid

The same result is achieved by ozonolysis, the reaction of an alkene with ozone, Eq. (15). An initially formed addition product,

$$\mathrm{CH_3\overset{\displaystyle CH_3}{\overset{|}{C}}{=}CHCH_3 + O_3 \rightarrow \left[CH_3\overset{\displaystyle CH_3}{\overset{|}{C}}{-}CHCH_3 \;(O_3\text{ bridging})\right] \rightarrow CH_3\overset{\displaystyle CH_3}{\overset{|}{C}}(O)(O{-}O)CHCH_3 \xrightarrow{H_2O} CH_3\underset{\underset{\displaystyle O}{\|}}{C}CH_3 + CH_3CHO + H_2O_2} \qquad (15)$$

an ozonide

acetone — acetaldehyde

which has been placed in brackets to indicate that its exact nature is not well-established, rearranges, with carbon-carbon cleavage, to a so-called ozonide. The latter can be decomposed with water to give the fragments shown.

In contrast to the substitution reactions of alkanes, which proceed only at high temperatures and result in fragmentation and more or less indiscriminate replacement of hydrogen, the addition reactions of alkenes and alkynes take place mainly at low temperature and involve only the π bond. Cleavage occurs only after addition and then specifically between the carbon atoms formerly linked by the double bond.

5–4 SUBSTITUTION REACTIONS OF ALCOHOLS AND HALOALKANES

Once a carbon-oxygen or carbon-halogen bond has been formed, however, substitution or displacement takes place relatively easily and specifically. This is shown by the following examples. Alcohols may be converted to haloalkanes, Eq. (16), or vice versa, Eq. (17):

$$\underset{\text{isobutyl alcohol}}{CH_3\overset{\overset{CH_3}{|}}{C}HCH_2OH} + HBr \rightarrow \underset{\text{isobutyl bromide}}{CH_3\overset{\overset{CH_3}{|}}{C}HCH_2Br} + H_2O \qquad (16)$$

$$CH_3\overset{\overset{CH_3}{|}}{C}HCH_2Br + NaOH \rightarrow CH_3\overset{\overset{CH_3}{|}}{C}HCH_2OH + NaBr \qquad (17)$$

Haloalkanes may yield a variety of useful products. Thus, treatment with inorganic cyanides furnishes nitriles, Eq. (18); with

(18) to (23):

$$CH_3\overset{\overset{CH_3}{|}}{C}HCH_2Br \xrightarrow[(18)]{KCN} CH_3\overset{\overset{CH_3}{|}}{C}HCH_2CN + KBr$$

$$CH_3\overset{\overset{CH_3}{|}}{C}HCH_2Br \xrightarrow[(19)]{NH_3} CH_3\overset{\overset{CH_3}{|}}{C}HCH_2CN + HBr$$

$$CH_3\overset{\overset{CH_3}{|}}{C}HCH_2Br \xrightarrow[(20)]{CH_3NH_2} CH_3\overset{\overset{CH_3}{|}}{C}HCH_2NHCH_3 + HBr$$

$$CH_3\overset{\overset{CH_3}{|}}{C}HCH_2Br \xrightarrow[(21)]{CH_3NHCH_3} CH_3\overset{\overset{CH_3}{|}}{C}HCH_2N(CH_3)_2 + HBr$$

$$CH_3\overset{\overset{CH_3}{|}}{C}HCH_2Br \xrightarrow[(22)]{NaSH} CH_3\overset{\overset{CH_3}{|}}{C}HCH_2SH + NaBr$$

$$CH_3\overset{\overset{CH_3}{|}}{C}HCH_2Br \xrightarrow[(23)]{Na_2S} CH_3\overset{\overset{CH_3}{|}}{C}HCH_2SCH_2\overset{\overset{CH_3}{|}}{C}HCH_3 + NaBr$$

ammonia, amines, Eq. (19); with amines, secondary, Eq. (20), or tertiary amines, Eq. (21); with sodium bisulfide, analogs of alcohols called mercaptans, Eq. (22); with sodium sulfide, sulfur analogs of ethers, Eq. (23), the sulfides, and so on. Ethers themselves are prepared by the reaction of haloalkanes with the class of compounds called sodium alkoxides, Eq. (25). These are formed from sodium metal and alcohols by a process, Eq. (24), which resembles the reaction of sodium with water:

$$2Na + 2CH_3CH_2OH \rightarrow \underset{\text{sodium ethoxide}}{2CH_3CH_2ONa} + H_2 \tag{24}$$

$$CH_3\overset{\overset{\displaystyle CH_3}{|}}{C}HCH_2Br + CH_3CH_2ONa \rightarrow \underset{\text{ethyl isobutyl ether}}{CH_3\overset{\overset{\displaystyle CH_3}{|}}{C}HCH_2OCH_2CH_3} + NaBr \tag{25}$$

Two Types of Substitution Reaction

What is the difference between the two types of substitution reaction? On the one hand, we have those rather random ones on alkanes which we must carry out at high temperature or under the influence of light. On the other hand, we have those on alcohols and haloalkanes which take place at moderate temperatures and result in exchange of one substituent for another. We can deduce immediately that substitution reactions on alkanes must require much energy because of the high temperatures which are necessary to get them started. On the other hand, substitution reactions on alcohols or haloalkanes appear to require much less energy, to judge by the temperatures employed.

5–5 BOND BREAKING AND BOND MAKING

The single feature which is common to all organic reactions is that, while new bonds are formed, old bonds are broken. For example, in the process of forming ethyl chloride from ethane by vapor-phase chlorination,

$$CH_3CH_2—H + Cl—Cl \rightarrow CH_3CH_2—Cl + H—Cl \quad (26)$$

one carbon-hydrogen bond and a chlorine-chlorine bond are broken, but a carbon-chlorine bond and a hydrogen-chlorine bond are formed. Similarly, in hydrolyzing ethyl chloride to ethyl alcohol, we break carbon-chlorine and hydrogen-hydroxyl bonds, but we form a carbon-hydroxyl and a hydrogen-chlorine bond:

$$CH_3CH_2—Cl + H—OH \rightarrow CH_3CH_2—OH + H—Cl \quad (27)$$

Breaking a bond requires energy; making a bond releases it. In general, the amount of energy which has to be supplied to start a reaction between organic molecules is far too small to cause complete dissociation of bonds between carbon atoms or between carbon and other elements. Obviously, part of the energy for the bond breaking comes from the bond making that is going on simultaneously. Whether the over-all reaction is exothermic (energy releasing) or endothermic (energy absorbing) depends on whether the energy total of all bonds being broken is less or greater than the energy total of all bonds being formed.

It is a relatively simple matter to calculate how much energy is required, or liberated, in a given reaction by considering the energies of all bonds being broken and formed. In turn, this should tell us something about the stability of the products. We might even conclude, somewhat hastily, that the more a given reaction releases energy, the more easily it should proceed.

However, if we apply this surmise to the two reactions mentioned above, we are in for a big surprise. It turns out that considerably more energy is released in reaction (26) than in reaction (27), which might lead us to predict that reaction (26) should proceed much more readily than reaction (27). Yet reaction (26) is very difficult to initiate compared with reaction (27). Once it does get started, however, reaction (26) is faster than reaction (27).

5–6 THE CONCEPT OF MECHANISM

The cause of our difficulty is that the ease of organic reactions is only rarely related to the exo- or endothermicity of the reaction. Only when the reaction is reversible and when equilibrium has been reached, i.e., when the velocity of the forward reaction is equal to the velocity of the reverse reaction, can we say that the proportion of starting materials and products depends on their relative stabilities. When this situation prevails, the products are said to be equilibrium-controlled. Similarly, when two or more products are produced from a given starting material and the reaction is equilibrium-controlled, the proportion of the products is only a function of their relative stabilities.

Most organic reactions are not reversible or, if they are reversible, they are not run under conditions which will permit establishment of equilibrium. In this situation, we are concerned not so much with the relative energies of starting materials and products, or with the relative energies of the several products, as with the rate at which the product is formed from starting material. If several products are produced, we are concerned with the relative rates at which each is formed from starting material. In the reaction

$$CH_3CH_2CH_3 + Cl_2 \rightarrow CH_3CH_2CH_2Cl + CH_3\underset{\displaystyle Cl}{\underset{|}{C}}HCl_3 \qquad (1)$$

for example, the proportion of 1- and 2-chloropropane making up the product depends not on the relative stability of 1- and 2-chloropropane, but on the rate at which chlorine is introduced into the CH_3— and the —CH_2— parts of the molecule. Such reactions are said to be kinetically controlled.

To explain these rates, we are interested in finding out for each particular reaction just how the reacting molecules are changed into the products. A description of the path by which they are transformed is called the mechanism of the reaction. The mechanism of chlorination of alkanes is obviously different from the mechanism of substitution in haloalkanes or alcohols.

It is important to point out that the mechanism of an organic reaction is simply a theory to account for the observations which we have made. The facts we need for our theory are gathered by studying the effect of different variables on the course of reaction. These variables include changes in temperature, changes in solvent, and slight changes in the reacting molecules. It is found, for example, that important changes in the rate of formation of hydrogen chloride take place if we substitute isopropyl chloride for ethyl chloride in Eq. (27). Similarly, rigid exclusion of oxygen from reaction (26) speeds up the reaction. This fact has to be accounted for if we wish to develop a satisfactory mechanism for the chlorination of alkanes.

Just as we increase our understanding of nature by isolating and studying the structure of the multitude of organic substances which she provides, so we hope to further our understanding by studying the chemical reactions which these and simpler compounds will undergo. The facts gathered in this manner will aid us in formulating mechanisms of organic reactions. In turn, an understanding of mechanisms may bring some order into the bewildering array of facts about organic compounds and how they behave. If our theories are sound, they may also aid us in a more practical way by enabling us to predict new reactions and new phenomena and by allowing us to control the old ones.

5-7 SUMMARY

Alkanes are relatively unreactive at room temperature, although they undergo substitution at higher temperatures. Alkenes and alkynes characteristically undergo addition reactions at moderate temperatures and can be oxidized. Alcohols and haloalkanes readily undergo substitution reactions.

To explain the varying ease of organic reactions and the directions taken by them, we can rely only rarely on calculations of energy differences. Instead, we are concerned with the relative rates of the reactions being studied. A hypothesis to explain these rates and the effect of different factors on them is called the reaction mechanism.

PROBLEMS

1. The energy required to break a covalent bond is also the energy released in forming it and is called the bond strength. The following table shows approximate bond strengths.

Bond	*Energy, kcal/mole*
C—C (single bond)	80
C=C (double bond)	145
C≡C (triple bond)	198
C—H	100
C—O	88
C—Cl	80
C—Br	65
H—H	103
H—Cl	103
H—Br	87
H—O	109
Cl—Cl	58
Br—Br	46

Calculate the over-all energy release (ΔH) for the following reactions:

(a) $H_2 + Br_2 \rightarrow 2HBr$
(b) hydrogenation of propylene
(c) addition of bromine to acetylene
(d) hydrohalogenation of isobutylene
(e) equations (27) and (28)
(f) hydration of propylene

2. Write equations analogous to Eqs. (19) through (24) and (26) for the reaction of 1-bromopropane, $CH_3CH_2CH_2Br$, with the appropriate reagents.

3. Write reactions analogous to Eqs. (5), (7), (9), (11), (13), (14) to (16) for

$$\begin{array}{c} \quad CH_3 \\ \quad | \\ CH_3C{=}CH{-}CH_3 \end{array}$$

2-methyl-2-butene

4. Write reactions analogous to Eqs. (6), (8), (10), and (12) for

$$HC{\equiv}C{-}CH_2CH_2CH_2CH_3$$

1-hexyne

VI

Making and Breaking Bonds—Radicals

In this brief introduction to organic chemistry it is obviously not possible to discuss in detail evidence for currently held theories on the mechanism of many different reactions. However, let us define a few terms and point out, in a simple way, how some of the reactions we have mentioned earlier are thought to proceed.

6–1 HOMOLYTIC AND HETEROLYTIC CLEAVAGE

In the first place, the bond breaking that occurs in the course of organic reactions may take place in two different ways. Homolytic or radical reactions are those reactions in which the bond is broken symmetrically, each of the partners retaining one of the electrons which formerly made up the bond. Heterolytic, or ionic, reactions are those reactions in which the bond is broken unsymmetrically, with one of the partners retaining both of the electrons. This is illustrated by Eqs. (1) and (2), in which the covalent bond is depicted by an electron pair.

Homolytic cleavage

$$X:Y \rightarrow X\cdot + Y\cdot \quad (1)$$

Heterolytic cleavage

$$X:Y \rightarrow X^+ + Y^- \quad (2)$$

6–2 RADICALS AND RADICAL CHAIN REACTIONS

The halogenation of ethane—and indeed this holds true for all substitution reactions of alkanes—is thought to be a homolytic reaction involving the following steps:

$$Cl:Cl \xrightarrow{\text{heat or light}} 2Cl\cdot \quad (3)$$

$$Cl\cdot + CH_3CH_3 \rightarrow CH_3CH_2\cdot + HCl \quad (4)$$

$$CH_3CH_2\cdot + Cl_2 \rightarrow CH_3CH_2Cl + Cl\cdot \quad (5)$$

$$Cl\cdot + CH_3CH_3 \rightarrow CH_3CH_2\cdot + HCl \quad (6)$$

etc.

The high temperature or the light supplies the energy for initiating the first, highly endothermic step, Eq. (3), in the course of which some chlorine molecules dissociate into atoms or radicals. A radical is an atom or group of atoms which has an unpaired electron.

Now radicals, by virtue of their unpaired electrons, are extremely reactive and seek to form new covalent bonds. The chlorine atom can do this by colliding with other atoms or molecules. Collision with another chlorine atom is unlikely because the concentration of such atoms is low. Collision with chlorine molecules is probable but results in no over-all change, since it produces another chlorine atom and another chlorine molecule. Collision with an ethane molecule, as in Eq. (4), results in the formation of a new radical, the ethyl radical, and a molecule of hydrogen chloride. The energy released in forming the hydrogen-chlorine bond just about compensates for the energy required to break the carbon-hydrogen bond.

The new ethyl radical is, in turn, highly reactive. Collisions with chlorine atoms or other ethyl radicals are improbable because of the low concentration of these species. Collision of the ethyl radicals with other ethane molecules results in no net change, Eq. (7):

$$CH_3CH_2\cdot + CH_3CH_3 \rightarrow CH_3CH_3 + CH_3CH_2\cdot \qquad (7)$$

But collision with a chlorine molecule, as in Eq. (5), is not only probable but furnishes a new chlorine atom which can and actually does continue the cycle until most of the chlorine has been used up.

We find that the energy in forming the carbon-chlorine bond more than compensates for the energy required to break the chlorine-chlorine bond. This results in an over-all energy release. In other words, the reaction is exothermic. The whole sequence, Eqs. (3) to (6), is an example of a chain reaction—a reaction which propagates itself because each of the steps produces a reactive substance, in this instance a radical, which brings about the next step.

In theory a chain reaction once started should continue indefinitely until the reagents are consumed. In practice, some of the more "improbable" collisions, such as chlorine atom with chlorine atom or ethyl radical with ethyl radical, occur often enough to terminate the chain. Hence it is frequently necessary to generate more radicals by keeping the temperature high or by irradiating with light, even though the reaction as a whole is exothermic. Similarly, if oxygen is present, reaction (8) can take place:

$$CH_3CH_2\cdot + O_2 \rightarrow CH_3CH_2—O_2\cdot \qquad (8)$$

The new radical is much less reactive than the ethyl radical and terminates the chain also.

6-3 ACTIVATION ENERGY

In any chemical reaction, whether it be the chlorination of ethane, the formation of ammonia from nitrogen and hydrogen, or the hydrolysis of ethyl bromide, collision between particles is not a guarantee that reaction will occur. Atoms and molecules are surrounded by negatively charged electron clouds. While they may deal each other surface blows, the repulsions caused by charges of the same sign do not allow the reacting particles to come within bond-forming distance unless they move fast enough to overcome this repulsion.

Again, even though the act of breaking and making a bond may result in an over-all energy release, the energy available from bond making (heat) is generally not completely available for bond breaking (for which kinetic energy is needed). As a consequence, if a reaction is to take place, the colliding particles must provide certain minimum energy over and above the average energy, which is called the *activation energy*. As the particles collide, their kinetic energy is converted to potential energy. This may result in the stretching of a bond, for example. If enough kinetic energy is available for conversion to potential energy, the bond may be stretched to the point at which the energy released in forming a new bond more than makes up for the energy needed to break the old one. Then reaction will occur. If, however, the moving particles do not have enough kinetic energy to reach this point, the collision remains fruitless.

The situation may be made clearer by reference to Fig. 6–1, which shows the energy changes that take place during a collision between a molecule of ethane and a molecule of chlorine. If enough kinetic energy is converted to potential energy, the top of the energy hill is reached and descent to the other side may start.

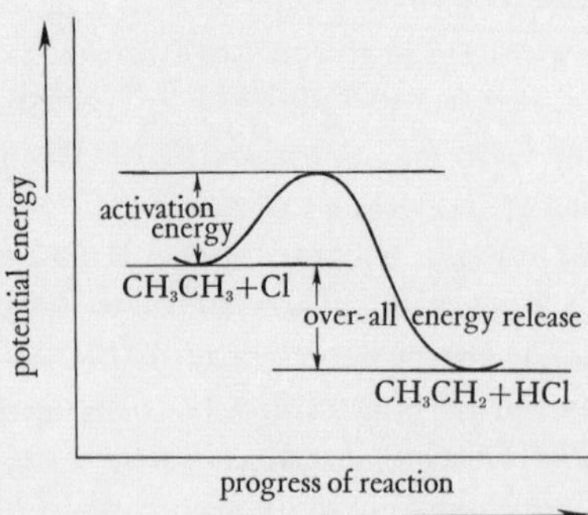

Figure 6–1 Energy changes during the chlorination of ethane, an exothermic reaction.

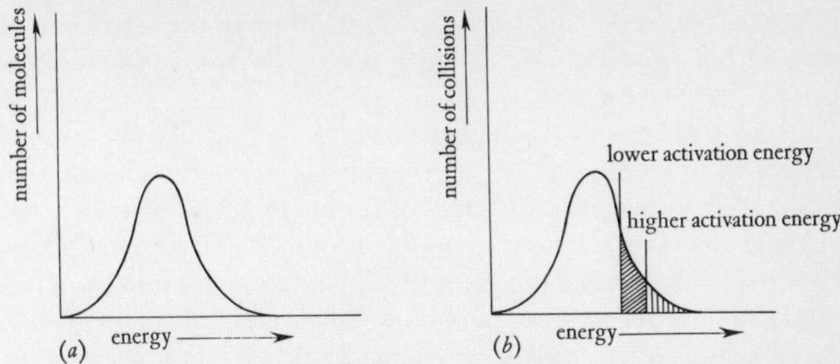

Figure 6–2 (*a*) **Distribution of kinetic energy among molecules and** (*b*) **distribution of kinetic energy among collisions.**

If not enough kinetic energy is provided, the top of the energy hill is not reached and the collision remains fruitless.

During the descent to the level of the products, potential energy is converted back to kinetic energy. Since the products contain less potential energy than the starting materials contained, there is an over-all increase in kinetic energy. This results in the liberation of heat.

Now, the distribution of kinetic energy among molecules is given by Fig. 6–2*a*. Since the kinetic energy of two colliding molecules is the sum of their respective kinetic energies, the distribution of kinetic energies among collisions is given by a similar curve (Fig. 6–2*b*), where the number of collisions with energy equal to or greater than E_{act} is indicated by the shaded area. As the activation energy becomes greater, the number of collisions which possess that energy becomes less. It can also be seen that by changing the value of E_{act} by a small amount we change the number of effective collisions by a large amount.

An increase in temperature raises the average kinetic energy of the molecules. The distribution of collision energies also changes, as indicated by the crossed curve of Fig. 6–3. This in turn results in an enormous increase of effective collisions and will increase the rate, or velocity, of the reaction being studied.

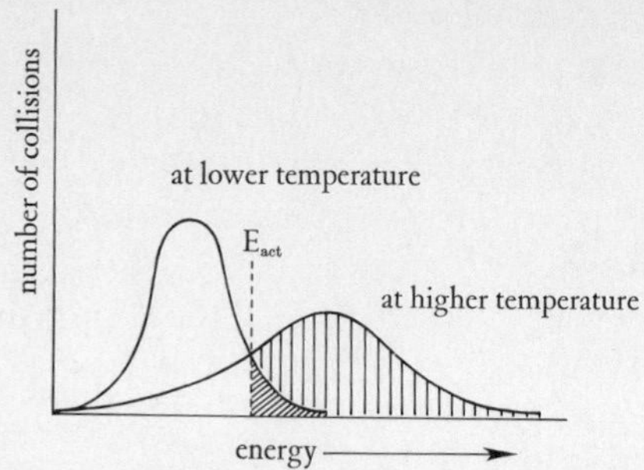

Figure 6–3 Change of collision energies with change in temperature.

6–4 ORIENTATION REQUIREMENT

In addition to requiring the energy which we have just discussed, the colliding particles must be properly oriented. For example, in the collision between an ethane molecule and a chlorine atom the ethane molecule must face the chlorine atom in a particular way to allow the latter to abstract hydrogen. Again, in the hydrolysis of ethyl chloride, water or hydroxide ion must approach the ethyl chloride molecule in a certain way in order to minimize the potential energy requirement. Approach from any other direction might theoretically lead to reaction also, but it would require a much larger energy input.

6–5 TRANSITION STATE

It is possible to imagine the reacting particles in the preferred orientation just at the instant when the bonds have been stretched to the required distance, the top of the hill in Fig. 6–1. At this point the reaction can proceed in either direction—forward to products or reverse to starting materials—without further increase in potential energy. The situation is analogous to that existing at a pass, or divide, between two mountain valleys. If a large beach ball is placed at the exact center of the divide, a very slight nudge can induce the ball to roll down in either direction.

The energy required to bring the reacting molecules to this pass or state—the so-called transition state—is the activation energy. Given a particular reaction path, we can describe the transition state as the most highly energetic and therefore most unstable configuration through which the reacting molecules must pass in order to become products.

It is obvious that a description of the transition state for any given reaction is entirely speculative, since by its very nature the transition state can never be isolated and studied. Nevertheless, the idea of such a state is useful. We can *a priori* write any number of different transition states for a given reaction. However, it will then be possible to estimate their stabilities relative to the initial, or ground, state and guess which would require the least activation energy. The one with the least activation energy would be the most likely. Any factor tending to stabilize the transition state would lower the energy of activation. This would be reflected in an increase in reaction rate and would thus be susceptible to test by experiment.

In this way, the abstraction of hydrogen from ethane by chlorine can be plausibly represented as in Eq. (9).

$$
\begin{array}{ccccc}
\mathrm{H} & & \mathrm{H} & & \mathrm{H} \\
| & & | & & | \\
\mathrm{CH_3C{-}H + Cl\cdot} & \rightarrow & \mathrm{CH_3C\cdots\cdots H\cdots\cdots Cl} & \rightarrow & \mathrm{CH_3C\cdot + HCl} \\
| & & | & & | \\
\mathrm{H} & & \mathrm{H} & & \mathrm{H} \\
\text{reactants} & & \text{transition state} & & \text{products}
\end{array} \qquad (9)
$$

The dotted lines in the transition state indicate that the carbon-hydrogen bond has been stretched but not yet broken and that the hydrogen-chlorine bond has not yet been completely formed. The products are hydrogen chloride and an ethyl radical. Because the latter has a relatively transitory existence and reacts further with a chlorine molecule in another reaction that has a transition state,

$$
\begin{array}{ccccc}
\mathrm{H} & & \mathrm{H} & & \\
| & & | & & \\
\mathrm{CH_3C\cdot + Cl{-}Cl} & \rightarrow & \mathrm{CH_3C\cdots\cdots Cl\cdots\cdots Cl} & \rightarrow & \mathrm{CH_3CH_2Cl + Cl\cdot} \\
| & & | & & \\
\mathrm{H} & & \mathrm{H} & & \\
\text{reactants} & & \text{transition state.} & & \text{products}
\end{array} \qquad (10)
$$

it is referred to as an intermediate. Other types of intermediates whose existence in organic reactions has been demonstrated are carbonium ions and carbanions (see Chap. VII).

6–6 SUMMARY

Covalent bonds may be broken in two ways: homolytic cleavage, which involves the formation of radicals, and heterolytic cleavage, which involves ionic intermediates.

Bonds are broken as the result of collisions between molecules. Not every collision results in the breaking of a bond. The rate of a reaction depends on the frequency of *effective* collisions. The frequency of effective collisions depends on whether the colliding particles have the proper orientation relative to each other (orientation requirement) and whether they have sufficient energy (energy requirement).

The extra potential energy needed to stretch the bonds so that reaction can occur is the activation energy. The lower the activation energy, the greater the number of effective collisions and therefore the greater the rate of the reaction, everything else being equal. A hypothetical description of the state of the colliding particles at the point of highest potential energy is called the transition state.

PROBLEMS

1. The reaction of methane with chlorine

$$CH_4 + Cl_2 \rightarrow CH_3Cl + HCl$$

is highly exothermic. Verify this by calculating ΔH for the reaction, using the table of bond energies on p. 58. Still the reaction does not proceed at room temperature, but requires a high temperature or light. Explain. [*Hint:* consider the ΔH's of the individual steps, analogous to Eqs. (4) to (7).]

2. Why is the mechanism on p. 60 more plausible than the following:

(a) $Cl_2 \rightarrow 2Cl$

(b) $Cl\cdot + CH_3CH_3 \rightarrow CH_3CH_2Cl + H$

(c) $H\cdot + Cl_2 \rightarrow HCl + Cl\cdot$ etc., etc.

3. What is the minimum energy that must be supplied to keep the bromination of methane going once it has been started? [*Hint:* consider the ΔH of the step analogous to Eq. (9).]

VII

Making and Breaking Bonds—Nucleophilic Substitution

Our introduction to the concept of reaction mechanism was motivated by the contrast between two apparently different types of *substitution* reaction. The first of these was the more or less random replacement of alkane hydrogen by halogen at high temperatures which, as has become clear by now, is a radical chain reaction. The second kind of substitution reaction was the specific replacement of halogen in haloalkanes by —OH, —NH_2, —CN, and so on, or of —OH in alcohols by halogen. These replacements take place under relatively mild conditions, generally in solution.

7–1 NUCLEOPHILES AND ELECTROPHILES

This second type of substitution reaction is called a nucleophilic substitution reaction because of the reagents which are used to replace the halogen or the hydroxyl. Nucleophiles, or nucleophilic reagents, are substances which form bonds with carbon by donating an electron pair to a site that is electron-deficient. They may be negatively charged ions like I^-, Br^-, OH^-, CN^-, and $CH_3CH_2O^-$ or acetate ion, or they may be neutral but with unshared electron pairs like water, alcohols, and ammonia. A third class of nucleophile is the class of carbanions: compounds containing negatively charged carbon. Electrophiles, or electrophilic reagents, on the other hand, are substances which form bonds with

$$\underset{\text{a carbanion}\atop \text{I}}{H{-}\overset{\displaystyle CN}{\underset{\displaystyle CN}{\overset{|}{\underset{|}{C^-}}}}} \qquad\qquad \underset{\text{a carbonium ion}\atop \text{II}}{CH_3CH_2\overset{\displaystyle CH_3}{\overset{|}{\underset{+}{C}}}CH_3}$$

carbon by accepting an electron pair. Examples of electrophiles are positively charged ions like protons and a number of substances containing elements with incomplete valence shells and empty orbitals like BF_3, SO_3, and $AlCl_3$. Carbonium ions—substances containing positively charged carbon whose existence as intermediates in organic reactions has been demonstrated—are also strong electrophiles.[1]

Examples of Nucleophilic Substitution

We are now ready to reconsider the reactions mentioned on pages 53 and 54. The hydrolysis of ethyl chloride by dilute sodium hydroxide solution, Eq. (1), involves displacement of chloride ion by the nucleophilic hydroxide ion, the preparation of ethylamine from ethyl chloride by displacement of chloride ion by the nucleophile ammonia, Eq. (2), and so on:

$$CH_3CH_2Cl + OH^- \rightarrow CH_3CH_2OH + Cl^- \tag{1}$$

$$CH_3CH_2Cl + NH_3 \rightarrow CH_3CH_2\overset{+}{N}H_3 + Cl^- \tag{2}$$

Similarly, the preparation of ethyl bromide from ethyl alcohol results from displacement of the hydroxyl group by the bromide ion in the following way:

[1] It should be pointed out that molecules which violate the tetravalence of carbon—carbanions, carbonium ions, and radicals—are so reactive that they cannot normally be isolated at room temperature.

$$CH_3CH_2OH + HBr \rightarrow CH_3CH_2\overset{+}{\underset{}{O}}(H)—H + Br^- \qquad (3)$$

$$CH_3CH_2\overset{+}{O}(H)H + Br^- \rightarrow CH_3CH_2Br + H_2O \qquad (4)$$

In the first step, Eq. (3), we have a simple acid-base reaction in which the unshared electron pair of the oxygen atom of ethyl alcohol serves as a proton acceptor. (Compare the self-ionization of water: $HOH + HOH \rightleftharpoons H_3O^+ + OH^-$.) The second step, Eq. (4), is the actual displacement of H_2O by the nucleophilic bromide ion.

Possible Mechanisms of Nucleophilic Substitution

Organic chemists have concluded that cleavage of the carbon-chlorine or carbon-hydroxyl bond in Eqs. (1), (2), and (4), is not homolytic, but heterolytic or ionic. The electron pair remains with the departing group. These reactions need not be initiated by light or high temperatures in the way that the chlorination of ethane is. They are not inhibited by oxygen, and they exhibit some of the other features characteristic of reactions involving radicals.

For an ionic cleavage, we can envisage two plausible possibilities:

1. The carbon-chlorine bond breaks first, giving us the type of intermediate which we have called a carbonium ion, Eq. (5). This would be followed by formation of a bond between the carbonium ion and the nucleophile, Eq. (6).

Two-step mechanism[1]

$$CH_3CH_2Cl \rightarrow \underset{\text{transition state}}{[CH_3\overset{\delta^+}{C}H_2\cdots\cdots\overset{\delta^-}{Cl}]} \rightarrow CH_3CH_2^+ + Cl^- \qquad (5)$$

$$CH_3CH_2^+ + OH^- \rightarrow CH_3CH_2OH \qquad (6)$$

[1] The δ^+ and δ^- signs indicate partial positive and negative charges which develop as the bond is being stretched. The electron pair moves with the chlorine.

2. We might consider the possibility of a one-step reaction in which formation of the new bond and breaking of the old one occurs more or less simultaneously, Eq. (7).

One-step mechanism

$$\mathrm{OH^-} + \begin{array}{c} \mathrm{CH_3} \\ \mathrm{H}\quad|\quad\mathrm{Cl} \\ \diagdown\,|\,\diagup \\ \mathrm{C} \\ | \\ \mathrm{H} \end{array} \rightarrow \left[\begin{array}{c} \mathrm{H}\qquad\mathrm{CH_3} \\ \delta^-\diagdown\ \diagup\qquad\delta^- \\ \mathrm{HO}\cdots\mathrm{C}\cdots\cdots\mathrm{Cl} \\ | \\ \mathrm{H} \end{array} \right] \rightarrow \begin{array}{c} \mathrm{CH_3} \\ \mathrm{HO}\quad|\quad\mathrm{H} \\ \diagdown\,|\,\diagup \\ \mathrm{C} \\ | \\ \mathrm{H} \end{array} + \mathrm{Cl^-} \qquad (7)$$

transition state

7-2 SOME CRITERIA FOR DETERMINING MECHANISMS—RATE

A number of criteria can be applied to determine which of the two paths described in the preceding section is operative. Consideration of one of these will be instructive. We note that in order to acquire enough energy to reach the transition state of the two-step mechanism, a molecule of ethyl chloride does not have to collide with a hydroxide ion. Any other molecule, for example, water, which is generally present in large excess will be just as good. Now the speed, or rate, of a reaction depends on the number of molecules which can reach the transition state in a given unit of time. Therefore, if the carbonium ion mechanism is correct, the rate of reaction should be dependent on the concentration of ethyl chloride, but independent of the concentration of hydroxide ion.[1]

On the other hand, the one-step mechanism requires collision, and a well-oriented one at that, between hydroxide ion and ethyl chloride in order to reach the transition state. Since the number of these collisions depends on the concentration of both partners, the correctness of the one-step mechanism would be established

---

[1] The rate would, of course, depend on the temperature, since temperature affects the kinetic energy of all colliding molecules, ethyl chloride, water, hydroxide ion, etc.

by showing that the rate of hydrolysis of ethyl chloride is dependent on the concentrations of both ethyl chloride and hydroxide ion.

It turns out that, for ethyl chloride at any rate, the rate of hydrolysis does indeed depend on the concentration of hydroxide ion as well as on the concentration of ethyl chloride. We therefore infer that the one-step mechanism is more plausible. However, nature does not allow us to generalize too much; for when we substitute *tert*-butyl chloride for ethyl chloride, we find that the rate of hydrolysis of this compound is independent of hydroxide ion concentration and is dependent only on the concentration of the chloride. Hence it seems that the hydrolysis of *tert*-butyl chloride proceeds by the two-step, or carbonium ion, mechanism.

In a quite similar way we can show that ethyl alcohol is converted to ethyl bromide by the one-stage process

$$CH_3CH_2OH + HBr \xrightarrow{\text{fast}} CH_3CH_2\overset{+}{O}H_2 + Br^- \qquad (8)$$

$$Br^- + \underset{H}{\overset{CH_3}{\underset{|}{\overset{|}{\underset{H\diagdown\quad\diagup\overset{+}{O}H_2}{C}}}}} \rightarrow \left[\underset{H}{\overset{H \qquad CH_3}{\overset{\delta-}{Br}\cdots\cdots \underset{|}{C} \cdots\cdots \overset{\delta+}{O}H_2}} \right] \rightarrow \underset{H}{\overset{CH_3}{\underset{|}{\overset{|}{\underset{Br\diagdown\quad\diagup H}{C}}}}} + H_2O \qquad (9)$$

transition state

whereas *tert*-butyl alcohol is transformed into *tert*-butyl bromide by the two-stage process

$$CH_3\overset{CH_3}{\underset{CH_3}{\overset{|}{\underset{|}{C}}}}\text{—}OH + HBr \xrightarrow{\text{fast}} CH_3\overset{CH_3}{\underset{CH_3}{\overset{|}{\underset{|}{C}}}}\text{—}\overset{+}{O}H_2 + Br^- \qquad (10)$$

$$CH_3\overset{CH_3}{\underset{CH_3}{\overset{|}{\underset{|}{C}}}}\text{—}\overset{+}{O}H_2 \rightarrow \left[CH_3\overset{CH_3}{\underset{CH_3}{\overset{|\,\delta+}{\underset{|}{C}}}}\cdots\cdots\overset{\delta+}{O}H_2 \right] \rightarrow CH_3\overset{CH_3}{\underset{CH_3}{\overset{|}{\underset{|}{C^+}}}} + H_2O \qquad (11)$$

transition state

$$\begin{array}{c} CH_3 \\ | \\ CH_3C^+ \\ | \\ CH_3 \end{array} + Br^- \rightarrow \begin{array}{c} CH_3 \\ | \\ CH_3C{-}Br \\ | \\ CH_3 \end{array} \tag{12}$$

We conclude that the paths by which apparently identical organic reactions proceed may depend quite profoundly on the structure of the reactants.

7-3 CRITERIA FOR DETERMINING MECHANISMS—PRODUCTS

As a matter of fact, an analysis of the products of a reaction may lead us to suspect a difference in mechanism before we have looked into the effect of concentration on rates. Consider, for example, the reaction of *n*-butyl bromide with sodium cyanide, which results in the formation of *n*-butyl cyanide:

$$CH_3CH_2CH_2CH_2Br + NaCN \xrightarrow[\text{and water}]{\text{ethanol}} CH_3CH_2CH_2CH_2CN + NaBr \tag{13}$$

On the other hand, reaction of the isomeric *tert*-butyl bromide with sodium cyanide under the same conditions gives little, if any, of the corresponding cyanide, but results mainly in isobutylene:

$$\begin{array}{c} CH_3 \\ | \\ CH_3CCH_3 \\ | \\ Br \end{array} \rightarrow \begin{array}{c} CH_3 \\ | \\ CH_3CCH_3 \\ + \end{array} \begin{array}{l} \xrightarrow{-H^+} \begin{array}{c} CH_3 \\ | \\ CH_3C{=}CH_2 \end{array} \\ \xrightarrow{+CN^-} \begin{array}{c} CH_3 \\ | \\ CH_3CCH_3 \\ | \\ CN \end{array} \end{array} \tag{14}$$

This seems to be the result of a difference in mechanism, a conclusion which can be verified by studying the rates. Normal butyl bromide reacts by the one-step process; the cyanide displaces the bromide ion by attacking carbon from the rear. Tertiary butyl bromide reacts by the two-step mechanism, the first step being formation of the *tert*-butyl carbonium ion.[1] In the second step there is competition between union with the bromide ion produced during the dissociation, union with cyanide ion, and, in a reaction which appears to be quite typical of carbonium ions, expulsion of a proton. The latter seems to be preferred and leads to isobutylene. The over-all result is not substitution, but elimination of hydrogen bromide.

Elimination may also occur as the result of a one-stage process, particularly when the nucleophile is strong and the temperature is high, as the following equation illustrates:

$$\underset{}{CH_3CH_2Br} + \underset{\text{sodium ethoxide}}{CH_3CH_2O^-Na^+} \xrightarrow[\text{in ethanol}]{55^\circ} \underset{\text{by substitution}}{CH_3CH_2OCH_2CH_3\ (90\%)} + \underset{\text{by elimination}}{CH_2{=}CH_2\ (10\%)} \quad (15)$$

One could explain this by assuming that two processes occur simultaneously, the one-stage displacement reaction and the formation of a carbonium ion which donates a proton to the sodium ethoxide. But we can show that a carbonium ion is not an intermediate in this reaction by measuring the rate at which ethylene is produced when the concentrations of ethyl bromide and sodium ethoxide are varied. The rate of formation of ethylene depends on the concentrations of both ethyl bromide and ethoxide ion. Hence both ethoxide ion and ethyl bromide are involved in the collision leading to the transition state. Equation (16) indicates the commonly accepted mechanism:

$$CH_3CH_2O^- + CH_3CH_2Br \rightarrow$$

$$CH_3CH_2{-}\overset{\delta^-}{O}\cdots H\cdots \underset{H}{\overset{H}{C}}\ \underline{\cdots\cdots}\ \underset{H}{\overset{H}{C}}\cdots \overset{\delta^-}{Br} \quad (16)$$

$$\downarrow$$

$$CH_3CH_2OH + CH_2{=}CH_2 + Br^-$$

---

[1] An answer to the obvious question why *tert*-butyl bromide forms a carbonium ion but *n*-butyl bromide does not will be found on page 77.

7-4 MOLECULAR REARRANGEMENTS

One other property of carbonium ions frequently complicates the study of displacement reactions. Consider, for example, the reaction of 2,2-dimethyl-1-propanol (III) with hydrogen bromide:

$$CH_3C(CH_3)_2CH_2OH + HBr \longrightarrow CH_3C(CH_3)_2CH_2Br$$

2,2-dimethyl-1-propanol (III) → 2,2-dimethyl-1-bromopropane (IV)

$$\downarrow +H^+$$

$$CH_3C(CH_3)_2CH_2\overset{+}{O}H_2 \qquad\qquad CH_3C(CH_3)(Br)CH_2CH_3 \quad (17)$$

2-bromo-2-methylbutane (V)

$$\downarrow -H_2O \qquad\qquad \uparrow$$

$$CH_3C(CH_3)_2CH_2^+ \longrightarrow CH_3\overset{+}{C}(CH_3)CH_2CH_3$$

A → B

Whether the reaction proceeds by the one- or two-stage process, we would expect the product to be 2,2-dimethyl-1-bromopropane (IV). In fact, however, investigation of the product shows it to be an isomeric substance, 2-bromo-2-methylbutane (V).

The halogen has not attached itself to the carbon atom which originally held the hydroxyl group, but even more surprising is the finding that the carbon skeleton of the product is quite different from that of the starting material. We say that the treatment of 2,2-dimethyl-1-propanol with hydrogen bromide has resulted in a molecular rearrangement.

The study of molecular rearrangements occupies an important place in organic chemistry. Although rearrangements are certainly unusual events, the possibility that a rearrangement may occur during a particular transformation can never be discounted completely and is one reason for the painstaking effort which the organic chemist devotes to proof of structure.

In the reaction illustrated by Eq. (17), for example, it will be necessary to distinguish the actual product, 2-bromo-2-methylbutane (V), from the expected 2,2-dimethyl-1-bromopropane (IV). Although this can be done by means of physical properties (boiling points, chromatographic behavior, absorption spectra, etc.), it is frequently difficult to do so, and recourse must be had to chemical properties. Thus, V can be converted by the route indicated in Eq. (19) to an acid which is easily distinguished from the acid obtained in a similar manner from IV, Eq. (18),[1] by its physical properties and by the preparation of so-called derivatives.

$$\underset{\text{IV}}{CH_3\overset{\overset{CH_3}{|}}{\underset{\underset{CH_3}{|}}{C}}CH_2Br} \xrightarrow[\text{ether}]{\text{Mg in}} \underset{\text{VI}}{CH_3\overset{\overset{CH_3}{|}}{\underset{\underset{CH_3}{|}}{C}}CH_2MgBr} \xrightarrow[\text{2. HBr}]{\text{1. }CO_2} CH_3\overset{\overset{CH_3}{|}}{\underset{\underset{CH_3}{|}}{C}}CH_2CO_2H + MgBr_2 \quad (18)$$

$$\underset{\text{V}}{CH_3\overset{\overset{CH_3}{|}}{\underset{\underset{Br}{|}}{C}}CH_2CH_3} \xrightarrow[\text{ether}]{\text{Mg in}} \underset{\text{VII}}{CH_3\overset{\overset{CH_3}{|}}{\underset{\underset{MgBr}{|}}{C}}CH_2CH_3} \xrightarrow[\text{2. HBr}]{\text{1. }CO_2} CH_3\overset{\overset{CH_3}{|}}{\underset{\underset{CO_2H}{|}}{C}}CH_2CH_3 + MgBr_2 \quad (19)$$

[1] Compounds VI and VII are prepared from the haloalkane by action of magnesium in dry ether, an example of the class of Grignard reagents. These substances, although hardly ever isolated, are exceedingly useful in synthesis.

7-5 CARBONIUM ION REARRANGEMENTS

Carbonium ions are particularly prone to rearrangement. The generally accepted mechanism for the rearrangement of 2,2-dimethyl-1-propanol is illustrated in Eq. (17). The first step is the usual acid-base reaction of the alcohol with aqueous hydrogen bromide. The second step leads to the carbonium ion which is the actual entity suffering the rearrangement, the methyl group migrating with a pair of electrons to the neighboring carbon atom. This generates a new carbonium ion which on union with the bromide ion yields the observed product.

We assume that the rearrangement takes place because the new carbonium ion B is more stable, i.e., of lower energy, than the old ion A. Now carbonium ions are classified as primary, secondary, or tertiary according to the groups on the positively charged carbon atom. Ion B, whose positively charged carbon atom carries three alkyl substituents other than hydrogen, is a tertiary carbonium ion. Ion A, whose positively charged carbon atom carries only one group other than hydrogen, is a primary carbonium ion. Ions which carry two groups other than hydrogen are secondary carbonium ions.

A good rule of thumb is that tertiary carbonium ions are more stable than secondary carbonium ions and that secondary carbonium ions are more stable than primary ones:

$$\begin{array}{c} \mathrm{R} \\ | \\ \mathrm{R{-}C^+} \\ | \\ \mathrm{R} \end{array} \quad \text{more stable than} \quad \begin{array}{c} \mathrm{R} \\ | \\ \mathrm{R{-}C^+} \\ | \\ \mathrm{H} \end{array} \quad \text{more stable than} \quad \begin{array}{c} \mathrm{H} \\ | \\ \mathrm{R{-}C^+} \\ | \\ \mathrm{H} \end{array}$$

The simplest explanation for this phenomenon is to consider the effect of an alkyl group on an adjacent positive charge. There is much support for the idea that, compared with hydrogen, an alkyl group tends to release electrons. Thus an alkyl group next to a positively charged carbon atom tends to release electrons to it. By doing so, it reduces the positive charge on its neighbor but becomes somewhat positive itself. This has the effect of distributing the positive charge over several atoms, a process that is supposed to increase the stability of the system. When two or three alkyl groups are attached to the positively charged carbon atom, each can release electrons to it and the positive charge is dispersed over a larger number of atoms.

7-6 SUMMARY

Nucleophiles are electron-rich reagents which form bonds with carbon by donating an electron pair. Electrophiles are substances with empty orbitals which form bonds with carbon by accepting an electron pair.

The reactions of alkyl halides with nucleophiles are typical nucleophilic substitution reactions. These may proceed by two mechanisms: (1) a one-step reaction involving two molecules in the process leading to the transition state, and (2) a two-step reaction involving only the alkyl halide in the process leading to the transition state. Criteria for these mechanisms are given. A side reaction which under certain conditions may predominate is the elimination reaction. Elimination may also proceed by a one-step reaction or a two-stage sequence.

The two-step substitution and elimination reactions involve carbonium ions as reactive intermediates.

PROBLEMS

1. Which of the following are nucleophiles, which electrophiles?

H_2O	BF_3	$(CH_3)_3N$
HCO_3^-	SO_2	F^-
CH_3^-	$(CH_3)_3C^+$	

2. Classify the following as to whether they are substitution or elimination reactions or whether they involve molecular rearrangements:

(a) $\underset{\displaystyle Br}{CH_3\overset{}{CH}}\text{—}\underset{\displaystyle Br}{CH_2} + KOH \text{ (in ethanol)} \rightarrow CH_3C{\equiv}CH$

$$\text{(b)}\quad \begin{array}{l}CH_3\\ |\\ CH_3CH{-}CH_2CH_2Br\end{array} + (CH_3)_2NH \rightarrow \begin{array}{l}CH_3\\ |\\ CH_3CH{-}CH_2CH_2N(CH_3)_2\end{array} + HBr$$

$$\text{(c)}\quad CH_3CH{=}CH{-}CH_2Br + KCN \rightarrow \begin{array}{l}CH_3{-}CH{-}CH{=}CH_2\\ \phantom{CH_3{-}}|\\ \phantom{CH_3{-}}CN\end{array}$$

$$\text{(d)}\quad \begin{array}{l}CH_2{-}CH{-}CH_2OH\\ |\qquad\ \ |\\ CH_2{-}CH_2\end{array} + H_2SO_4 \rightarrow \begin{array}{ccc} & H_2C & \\ & / \quad \backslash & \\ H_2C & & CH\\ | & & \|\\ H_2C & \text{———} & CH\end{array}$$

3. Primary alcohols are alcohols of the type $R{-}CH_2OH$. Secondary alcohols may be represented by $R_2{-}CHOH$ and tertiary alcohols by $R_3{-}COH$, where R is a group other than hydrogen. A good test for distinguishing between the three classes of alcohols consists of treating the unknown alcohol with a solution of zinc chloride in concentrated hydrochloric acid according to the equation:

$$R{-}CH_2OH + HCl \xrightarrow{ZnCl_2} R{-}CH_2Cl + H_2O$$

Would primary, secondary, or tertiary alcohols react the fastest? Explain your answer.

VIII

Making and Breaking Bonds—Addition

In the preceding chapter we developed the concept of reaction mechanism by considering two different types of substitution reactions. Of equal importance, from a practical and theoretical standpoint, are the addition reactions which, as we saw in Chap. IV, are characteristic of molecules containing π (double or triple) bonds.

8-1 TWO TYPES OF ADDITION REACTIONS

Superficially, the addition reactions of alkenes (and alkynes) seem to be very similar to the addition reactions of aldehydes, ketones, esters, amides, nitriles, and so on. In both instances the breaking of one π bond results in the formation of two new σ bonds, one to each of the atoms previously linked by the π bond. As a matter of fact, however, most additions to alkenes and alkynes involve initial attack by an electrophilic species (for definition see page 69), and they are therefore called electrophilic addition reactions. On the other hand, additions to multiple bonds between carbon and some other element (oxygen as in aldehydes, ketones, esters, and amides; nitrogen as in nitriles or imines)

Typical addition reactions of an alkene

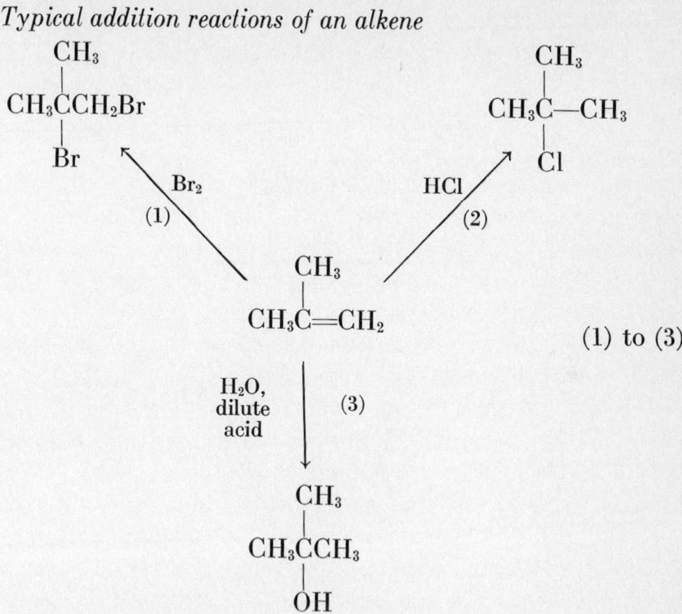

(1) to (3)

Typical addition reactions of an aldehyde

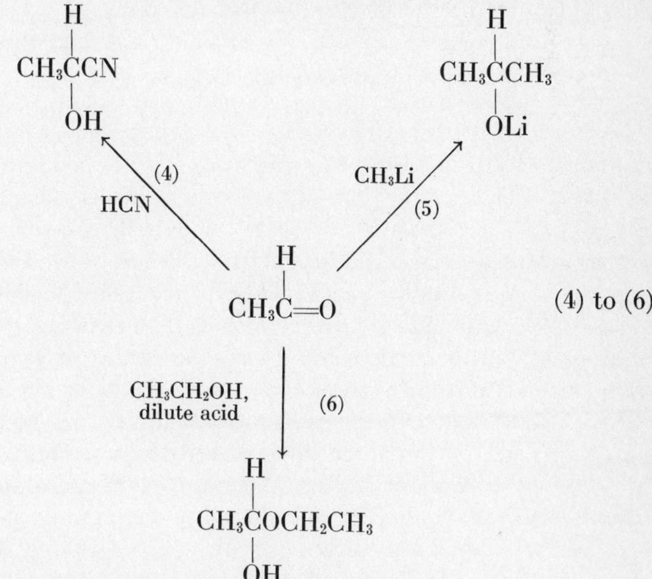

(4) to (6)

generally involve attack on carbon by nucleophilic reagents and are classified as nucleophilic addition reactions.

8–2 POLARITY OF COVALENT BONDS

Why do the two types of double bond behave differently toward nucleophiles and electrophiles? An explanation, which seems to do justice to this and other related phenomena, depends on the concept that covalent bonds between two atoms of different electronegativity exhibit a certain degree of polarity.

We have already mentioned the origin of this idea briefly on p. 20. In a molecule of hydrogen chloride, for example, the center of positive charge does not coincide with the center of negative charge. The hydrogen chloride molecule constitutes a dipole and is said to be polar. In a similar way, methyl chloride (CH_3Cl), ethanol (CH_3CH_2OH) and many other organic substances exhibit a greater or lesser degree of polarity. The polarity of the molecule as a whole is assumed to be due to the polarity of some of the bonds within it. We can expect a covalent bond to be polar if it joins two atoms of different electronegativity, say, hydrogen and chlorine or carbon and either oxygen or nitrogen.

8–3 BASICITY OF ALKENES

As a first approximation, the carbon-carbon bonds which make up the skeletons of simple hydrocarbons may be assumed to be nonpolar. Whether the carbon atoms are joined by single, double, or triple bonds would appear to make little difference, since two atoms of the same electronegativity are involved. Hence the two sp^2- or sp-hybridized carbon atoms of alkenes and alkynes, respectively, offer equally likely targets for incoming reagents which would not be expected to discriminate between them. And since the electrons of alkenes are relatively loosely held, and hence available for covalent bond formation, the type of reagent with which alkenes would be likely to interact is electrophilic, i.e., capable of accommodating a pair of electrons in its outer valence shell.

According to this view, alkenes and alkynes are electron-pair donors or bases. Their degree of basicity depends on the availability of their π electrons, which in turn can be influenced by the substituents attached to the sp^2- or sp-hybridized carbon atoms.

8-4 MECHANISM OF ELECTROPHILIC ADDITION TO ALKENES

In the relatively simple case of isobutylene, the addition of hydrogen chloride, for example, is believed to proceed by way of Eqs. (7) and (8):

$$CH_3\overset{\overset{\displaystyle CH_3}{|}}{C}{=}CH_2 + HCl \rightarrow CH_3\underset{+}{\overset{\overset{\displaystyle CH_3}{|}}{C}}CH_3 + Cl^- \tag{7}$$

$$CH_3\underset{+}{\overset{\overset{\displaystyle CH_3}{|}}{C}}CH_3 + Cl^- \rightarrow CH_3\underset{\underset{\displaystyle Cl}{|}}{\overset{\overset{\displaystyle CH_3}{|}}{C}}CH_3 \tag{8}$$

In the first step, Eq. (7), the electrophilic reagent, a proton, attacks the π electrons of the double bond in such a manner as to give, finally, the most stable carbonium ion. In this process a new acid, the carbonium ion, and a new base, the chloride ion, have been generated. In the second step, Eq. (8), the new acid and the new base unite to form the product.

The hydration of isobutylene under the influence of an acid catalyst, Eq. (3), is believed to proceed similarly if we make allowance for details of mechanism which need not concern us here. And although it is difficult to visualize a bromide or chlorine molecule as an electrophilic species, the evidence is overwhelming that interaction of the π-electron cloud of the alkene with the halogen molecule results in the formation of a halogen dipole by a process which we call polarization: the distortion of the electron distribution in the halogen molecule by the alkene. The more positive end of this induced dipole then reacts with the alkene and forms what has been represented in a somewhat oversimplified fashion as a carbonium ion and a halide ion:

$$\begin{array}{c} CH_3 \quad CH_3 \\ \diagdown \; \diagup \\ C \\ \| \\ C \\ \diagup \; \diagdown \\ H \quad\;\; H \end{array} \quad \overset{\delta^+}{Br} - \overset{\delta^-}{Br} \rightarrow \quad \begin{array}{c} CH_3 \quad CH_3 \\ \diagdown \; \diagup \\ C^+ \\ | \\ CH_2Br \end{array} \quad + Br^- \qquad (9)$$

These two then combine in the second step to form the product:

$$\begin{array}{c} CH_3 \quad CH_3 \\ \diagdown \; \diagup \\ C^+ \\ | \\ CH_2Br \end{array} \quad + Br^- \rightarrow \quad \begin{array}{c} CH_3 \quad CH_3 \\ \diagdown \; \diagup \\ C{-}Br \\ | \\ CH_2Br \end{array} \qquad (10)$$

8–5 THE ELECTROPHILIC NATURE OF THE CARBONYL CARBON

Let us now consider a molecule which contains a carbon-oxygen double bond, e.g., an aldehyde or an ester. In contrast to the situation we have just discussed, the double bond now connects two atoms of widely different electronegativity. We can infer from considering the physical properties (boiling points, solubilities, dipole moments) of alcohols and ethers that a carbon-oxygen single bond is decidedly polar. We would therefore expect that the more mobile π electrons of the carbon-oxygen double bond would be even more readily displaced toward oxygen. Since this polarization depletes the electron supply around the carbonyl carbon atom, the carbonyl carbon becomes electrophilic and is readily attacked by nucleophiles. Conversely, the oxygen atom of the carbonyl group becomes somewhat nucleophilic, or basic, and may offer a suitable target for electrophiles.

8–6 MECHANISM OF NUCLEOPHILIC ADDITION TO ALDEHYDES

The three reactions of acetaldehyde given on p. 81 may be interpreted on this basis. The addition of hydrogen cyanide, Eq. (4), seems to involve initial attack on carbon by cyanide ion, a nucleophile, Eq. (11), followed by reaction of the oxygen anion with the proton, Eq. (12).

$$CH_3\overset{\displaystyle H}{\overset{|}{C}}{=}O + HCN \rightarrow CH_3\underset{\displaystyle CN}{\underset{|}{\overset{\displaystyle H}{\overset{|}{C}}}}{-}O^- + H^+ \tag{11}$$

$$CH_3\underset{\displaystyle CN}{\underset{|}{\overset{\displaystyle H}{\overset{|}{C}}}}{-}O^- + H^+ \rightarrow CH_3\underset{\displaystyle CN}{\underset{|}{\overset{\displaystyle H}{\overset{|}{C}}}}OH \tag{12}$$

The second illustration, Eq. (5), the reaction with methyl lithium, obeys the same principle. The carbon-lithium bond is highly polarized, carbon being much more electronegative than strongly electropositive lithium. It is therefore not surprising that the methyl group attaches itself to carbon and lithium attaches itself to oxygen:

$$CH_3\overset{\displaystyle H}{\overset{|}{C}}{=}O + CH_3{-}Li \rightarrow CH_3\underset{\displaystyle CH_3}{\underset{|}{\overset{\displaystyle H}{\overset{|}{C}}}}OLi \tag{13}$$

Incidentally, the product is the lithium salt of an alcohol to which it may be converted by hydrolysis with an aqueous solution of an acid:

$$CH_3\underset{\displaystyle CH_3}{\underset{|}{\overset{\displaystyle H}{\overset{|}{C}}}}OLi + HCl \rightarrow CH_3\underset{\displaystyle CH_3}{\underset{|}{\overset{\displaystyle H}{\overset{|}{C}}}}OH + LiCl \tag{14}$$

The reaction of an aldehyde or ketone with an organolithium[1] compound thus affords a route to many different types of alcohols.

[1] The corresponding organomagnesium derivatives, called the Grignard reagents, are used more often for this purpose. Since magnesium is divalent, their formula is generally written as RMgX or R_2Mg.

8–7 CATALYSIS OF NUCLEOPHILIC ADDITION

The third reaction, Eq. (6), the formation of a so-called hemiacetal from acetaldehyde and ethanol, illustrates the catalytic effect of acids on the nucleophilic addition reactions of carbonyl compounds. The reactions of protons or other strong electrophiles with the negatively polarized oxygen atom, Eq. (15), enhances the electrophilic properties of the carbonyl carbon (that is, makes the carbon atom more positive) and allows it to react with the relatively weak nucleophile ethyl alcohol, Eq. (16). In the last step, the proton catalyst is regenerated, Eq. (17):

$$CH_3\overset{\overset{\large H}{|}}{C}{=}O + H^+ \rightleftharpoons CH_3\underset{+}{\overset{\overset{\large H}{|}}{C}}{-}OH \qquad (15)$$

$$CH_3\underset{+}{\overset{\overset{\large H}{|}}{C}}{-}OH + CH_3CH_2OH \rightleftharpoons CH_3\underset{\underset{\underset{+}{HOCH_2CH_3}}{|}}{\overset{\overset{\large H}{|}}{C}}{-}OH \qquad (16)$$

$$CH_3\underset{\underset{\underset{+}{HOCH_2CH_3}}{|}}{\overset{\overset{\large H}{|}}{C}}{-}OH \rightleftharpoons CH_3\underset{\underset{OCH_2CH_3}{|}}{\overset{\overset{\large H}{|}}{C}}{-}OH + H^+ \qquad (17)$$

a hemiacetal

8–8 NUCLEOPHILIC ADDITION TO OTHER TYPES OF COMPOUNDS

Nucleophilic additions to carbon-nitrogen double and triple bonds can be explained similarly. But since nitrogen is not as electronegative as oxygen, the permanent polarization of the carbon-nitrogen double bond is not as great and the carbon atom of such compounds is not as susceptible to attack by nucleophiles as in aldehydes or ketones.

Somewhat earlier, several other classes of compounds were listed as also containing a carbonyl group, page 41. These include the acids, the esters, the amides, and the acyl halides, some representatives of which are given in formulas I to IV. The chemical behavior of these compounds depends on the carbonyl group which,

$$CH_3CH_2CH_2\overset{\overset{\displaystyle O}{\|}}{C}—OH$$

butyric acid or
butanoic acid
I

$$CH_3CH_2\overset{\overset{\displaystyle O}{\|}}{C}—OCH_3$$

methyl propionate,
an ester
II

$$CH_3\overset{\overset{\displaystyle O}{\|}}{C}—NH_2$$

acetamide,
an amide
III

$$CH_3CH_2\overset{\overset{\displaystyle O}{\|}}{C}—Cl$$

propionyl chloride,
an acyl halide
IV

in analogy to the behavior of aldehydes and ketones, might be expected to encourage nucleophilic addition. This is indeed the case, but the intermediates produced in this way are generally not stable and cannot be isolated. The end result is one of substitution.

8–9 REACTIONS OF ACYL HALIDES

The statement concluding the preceding paragraph can be illustrated by the reaction of an acyl halide, propionyl chloride (IV), with methyl alcohol. In the first step, Eq. (18), nucleophilic attack on the acyl chloride by an alcohol molecule results in addition to the π bond. The unstable intermediate expels a chloride ion, Eq. (19), which in turn takes up the extra proton, Eq. (20). The net effect is the exchange of $—OCH_3$ for —Cl and the formation of an ester:

$$CH_3CH_2\overset{\overset{\displaystyle O}{\|}}{C}—Cl + CH_3OH \rightarrow CH_3CH_2\underset{\underset{\underset{+}{\displaystyle HOCH_3}}{|}}{\overset{\overset{\displaystyle O^-}{|}}{C}}—Cl \tag{18}$$

$$CH_3CH_2\underset{\underset{\underset{+}{\displaystyle HOCH_3}}{|}}{\overset{\overset{\displaystyle O^-}{|}}{C}}—Cl \rightarrow CH_3CH_2\overset{\overset{\displaystyle O}{\|}}{C}—\underset{\underset{\displaystyle H}{|}}{\overset{+}{O}}CH_3 + Cl^- \tag{19}$$

$$CH_3CH_2\overset{\overset{\displaystyle O}{\|}}{C}\text{—}\underset{\underset{\displaystyle H}{|}}{\overset{+}{O}}CH_3 + Cl^- \rightarrow CH_3CH_2\overset{\overset{\displaystyle O}{\|}}{C}\text{—}OCH_3 + HCl \qquad (20)$$

In the same way, acyl halides react with ammonia to form amides, Eqs. (21) to (23), and with water or hydroxide ion to form acids, Eqs. (24) to (26). In the last step of the hydrolysis of an acyl chloride, Eq. (26), the organic acid reacts with excess

$$CH_3CH_2\overset{\overset{\displaystyle O}{\|}}{C}\text{—}Cl + NH_3 \rightarrow CH_3CH_2\underset{\underset{\displaystyle \underset{+}{NH_3}}{|}}{\overset{\overset{\displaystyle O^-}{|}}{C}}\text{—}Cl \qquad (21)$$

$$CH_3CH_2\underset{\underset{\displaystyle \underset{+}{NH_3}}{|}}{\overset{\overset{\displaystyle O^-}{|}}{C}}\text{—}Cl \rightarrow CH_3CH_2\overset{\overset{\displaystyle O}{\|}}{C}\text{—}\overset{+}{N}H_3 + Cl^- \qquad (22)$$

$$CH_3CH_2\overset{\overset{\displaystyle O}{\|}}{C}\text{—}\overset{+}{N}H_3 + NH_3 \rightarrow CH_3CH_2\overset{\overset{\displaystyle O}{\|}}{C}\text{—}NH_2 + NH_4^+ \qquad (23)$$

$$CH_3CH_2\overset{\overset{\displaystyle O}{\|}}{C}\text{—}Cl + OH^- \rightarrow CH_3CH_2\underset{\underset{\displaystyle OH}{|}}{\overset{\overset{\displaystyle O^-}{|}}{C}}\text{—}Cl \qquad (24)$$

$$CH_3CH_2\underset{\underset{\displaystyle OH}{|}}{\overset{\overset{\displaystyle O^-}{|}}{C}}\text{—}Cl \rightarrow CH_3CH_2\overset{\overset{\displaystyle O}{\|}}{C}\text{—}OH + Cl^- \qquad (25)$$

$$CH_3CH_2\overset{\overset{\displaystyle O}{\|}}{C}\text{—}OH + OH^- \rightarrow CH_3CH_2\overset{\overset{\displaystyle O}{\|}}{C}\text{—}O^- + H_2O \qquad (26)$$

hydroxide ion, a strong base, to form the weaker base carboxylate ion and the weaker acid water.[1]

8-10 ACIDS AND ESTERS

Quite similarly, acids react with alcohols in the presence of acid catalysts to form esters, Eqs. (27) to (29), which are hydrolyzed by the reverse process or by treatment with aqueous base, Eqs. (30) and (31). In this way groups like —Cl, —OR, —NH_2, and —OH, which are attached to a carbonyl carbon atom, can be replaced by some other nucleophile.

Esterification and acid hydrolysis

$$R\text{—}\overset{\overset{\displaystyle O}{\|}}{C}\text{—}OH + H^+ \rightarrow R\text{—}\underset{+}{\overset{\overset{\displaystyle OH}{|}}{C}}\text{—}OH \tag{27}$$

$$R\text{—}\underset{+}{\overset{\overset{\displaystyle OH}{|}}{C}}\text{—}OH + R'OH \rightarrow R\text{—}\underset{\underset{\overset{\displaystyle HOR'}{+}}{|}}{\overset{\overset{\displaystyle OH}{|}}{C}}\text{—}OH \tag{28}$$

[1] This reaction of carboxylic acids is not limited to hydroxide ion but takes place with any base whose conjugate acid is weaker than the carboxylic acid. Thus, acetic acid reacts with ammonia to form ammonium acetate,

$$CH_3CO_2H + NH_3 \rightarrow CH_3\underset{\underset{\displaystyle O}{\|}}{C}\text{—}O^- + NH_4^+$$

and with organic bases such as amines to form the corresponding salts:

$$CH_3CO_2H + N(CH_3)_3 \rightarrow CH_3\underset{\underset{\displaystyle O}{\|}}{C}\text{—}O^- + H\overset{+}{N}(CH_3)_3$$

From these salts, the acids can be regenerated by treatment with mineral acids:

$$CH_3\underset{\underset{\displaystyle O}{\|}}{C}\text{—}O^- + NH_4^+ \xrightarrow{HCl} CH_3CO_2H + NH_4^+ + Cl^-$$

$$CH_3\underset{\underset{\displaystyle O}{\|}}{C}\text{—}O^- + H\overset{+}{N}(CH_3)_3 \xrightarrow{HCl} CH_3CO_2H + H\overset{+}{N}(CH_3)_3 + Cl^-$$

$$\underset{\underset{+}{\text{HOR}'}}{\overset{\text{OH}}{\text{R—}\underset{|}{\overset{|}{\text{C}}}\text{—OH}}} \rightarrow \text{R—}\underset{\underset{\text{O}}{\|}}{\text{C}}\text{—OR}' + H_3O^+ \qquad (29)$$

Basic hydrolysis of an ester (saponification)

$$\text{R—}\overset{\overset{\text{O}}{\|}}{\text{C}}\text{—OR}' + OH^- \rightarrow \text{R—}\underset{\underset{\text{OH}}{|}}{\overset{\overset{\text{O}^-}{|}}{\text{C}}}\text{—OR}' \qquad (30)$$

$$\text{R—}\underset{\underset{\text{OH}}{|}}{\overset{\overset{\text{O}^-}{|}}{\text{C}}}\text{—OR}' \rightarrow \text{R—}\overset{\overset{\text{O}}{\|}}{\text{C}}\text{—O}^- + \text{R'OH} \qquad (31)$$

8–11 SUMMARY

Addition reactions of alkenes are interpreted as involving the attack of electron-poor, or electrophilic, reagents on the electron-rich, or nucleophilic, double bond.

Addition reactions of compounds containing a carbonyl group are interpreted as involving the attack of nucleophilic reagents on the electrophilic carbon atom of the carbonyl group. Such reactions can be catalyzed by acids and by bases.

PROBLEMS

1. Write equations for the following addition reactions:

(a) $CH_3\text{—}\overset{\overset{CH_3}{|}}{CH}\text{—}CH_2CH{=}CH_2 + HCl \rightarrow$

(b) $CH_3CH_2CH{=}CH\text{—}CH_2CH_3 + Br_2 \rightarrow$

(c) $CH_3\overset{\overset{CH_3}{|}}{CH}\text{—}CH_2\overset{\overset{H}{|}}{C}{=}O + CH_3Li \rightarrow$

(d) $CH_3CH_2CH_2\overset{H}{\overset{|}{C}}{=}O + CH_3CH_2OH \xrightarrow{H^+}$

(e) $CH_3CH_2CH_2\overset{O}{\overset{\|}{C}}{-}Cl + CH_3CH_2OH \rightarrow$

(f) $CH_3\overset{CH_3}{\overset{|}{C}}H{-}CH_2\overset{O}{\overset{\|}{C}}{-}Cl + NH_3 \rightarrow$

(g) $CH_3CH_2CH_2\overset{O}{\overset{\|}{C}}{-}OH + CH_3OH \xrightarrow{H^+}$

(h) $CH_3CH_2\overset{O}{\overset{\|}{C}}{-}OCH_3 + OH^- \rightarrow$

2. Treatment of $CH_3{-}\underset{CH_3}{\underset{|}{\overset{CH_3}{\overset{|}{C}}}}{-}CH{=}CH_2$ with aqueous mineral acid results in the formation of some $CH_3{-}\underset{H}{\underset{|}{\overset{CH_3}{\overset{|}{C}}}}{-}\underset{OH}{\underset{|}{\overset{CH_3}{\overset{/}{C}}}}{-}CH_3$. Can you suggest an explanation?

IX

Delocalization of π Electrons—Resonance

OUR CURSORY REVIEW of the structure and chemistry of alkanes, alkenes, and alkynes indicated that alkanes and cycloalkanes could be differentiated from their olefinic and acetylenic cousins by a few simple chemical tests. For example, although cyclohexane and the several isomeric hexenes have the same empirical formula, C_6H_{12}, cyclohexane remains chemically inert toward bromine and potassium permanganate solution, while the red color of bromine or the purple color of the oxidizing agent disappears rapidly on admixture of the hexenes.

9-1 BENZENE

A compound of formula C_6H_6 would, we might expect, exhibit the properties of alkenes or alkynes to an enhanced degree, since the empirical formula indicates the presence of several double or triple bonds. Several such compounds of formula C_6H_6 have been synthesized in recent years, and they behave just about as predicted. But one substance of formula C_6H_6, benzene, has been known for a very long time and, contrary to expectations, shows not the slightest similarity to alkenes and alkynes.

Reactions of Benzene

Benzene, its derivatives, and its homologs do not undergo the addition reactions with which we have become familiar. They remain inert toward halogens, hydrogen, or oxidizing reagents under conditions which rapidly transform olefins or acetylenes. On the other hand, substitution of hydrogen—so difficult in the case of alkanes or cycloalkanes—may be affected comparatively readily under conditions which obviously do not involve radical chain reactions. Some of these reactions are given in Eqs. (1) to (6).

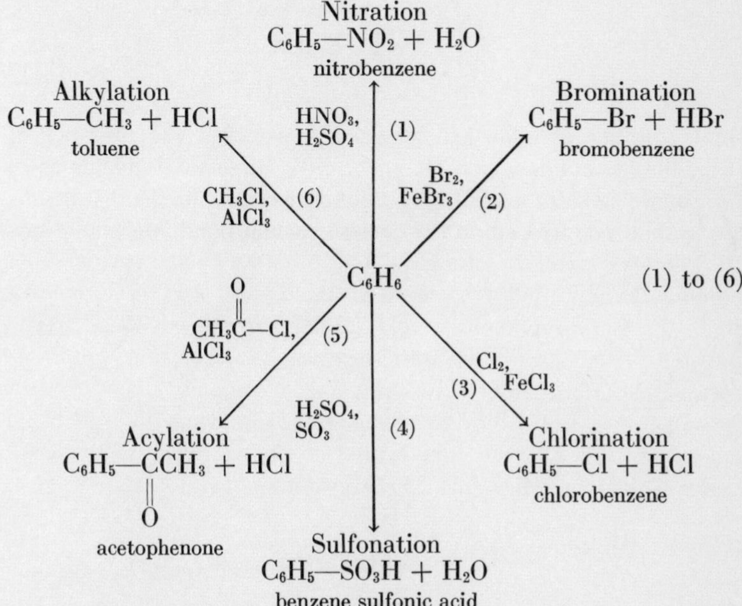

Because of these characteristics, benzene and compounds which resemble benzene in chemical behavior are differentiated from the substances we have discussed so far, the so-called aliphatics, and are known as aromatic compounds.[1]

[1] The adjectives aliphatic (fatty) and aromatic (fragrant) were used originally because they denoted characteristic properties of representative compounds.

Structural Formula of Benzene—Isomer Number

It can be shown quite readily that benzene must be cyclic and that the ring contains six carbon atoms. For example, catalytic hydrogenation of benzene at high pressure and temperature yields cyclohexane. We could, then, account for the

```
                                   H₂
                                   C
                                 /   \
             high pressure   H₂C       CH₂
    C₆H₆ ------------------>   |         |          (7)
               H₂, Ni        H₂C       CH₂
                                 \   /
                                   C
                                   H₂
```

small number of hydrogen atoms by assuming the presence of three double bonds which alternate with three single bonds as in Ia (Ib and Ic seem exceedingly unlikely because of the distortions that would be imposed on the carbon-carbon bond angles). Since

```
        H                    H                       H
        |                    |                       |
  H     C     H              C     H                 C      H
   \  //  \  /             /  \\  /                //  \   /
    C       C             C     C                 C      C
    |       ||            |||   |                 ||     ||
    C       C             C     CH₂               C      C
   /  \\  /  \             \   /                /  \   /  \
  H     C     H              C               H      C      H
        |                    H₂                     H₂
        H
        Ia                   Ib                     Ic
```

all hydrogens of Ia are equivalent, we would expect to find only one mono-substitution product, say, C_6H_5Br, when one of the six hydrogen atoms is replaced by bromine. Indeed, only one monobromobenzene seems to be formed.

How many isomers should we expect on replacing two hydrogen atoms by bromine? At first glance only three, depending on whether the bromine atoms are attached to adjacent carbons as in II, the so-called 1,2-dibromo derivative, or to more widely separated carbons as in III, the 1,3-dibromo compound, or IV, the 1,4-derivative. But II is not unique. An equally likely

```
         Br                    Br
         |                     |
  H      C      Br      H      C      H
   \   /   \\  /         \   /   \\  /
     C       C             C       C
     ||      |             ||      |
     C       C             C       C
   /   \   //  \         /   \   //  \
  H      C      H       H      C      Br
         |                     |
         H                     H
        II                    III

         Br                    Br
         |                     |
  H      C      H       H      C      Br
   \   /   \\  /         \   //  \   /
     C       C             C       C
     ||      |             |       ||
     C       C             C       C
   /   \   //  \         /   \\  /   \
  H      C      H       H      C      H
         |                     |
         Br                    H
        IV                     V
```

1,2-dibromo formula would be V, which differs from II in the position of the bromine atoms relative to the double bond. In spite of diligent searching, however, only three dibromobenzenes have been found, one 1,2-, one 1,3-, and one 1,4-dibromobenzene. It appears, therefore, that the representation of benzene as Ia, which we might call cyclohexatriene, is in error, not only because the properties of benzene do not correspond to those of an alkene, but also because Ia leads us to expect the wrong number of derivatives.

Shape of Benzene Molecule

Now X-ray and electron diffraction experiments show that benzene is a flat, completely symmetrical molecule. The six

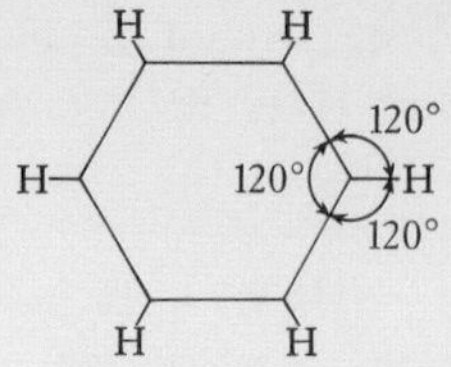

Figure 9–1 Shape of benzene molecule.

carbon-carbon bonds are of equal length and all bond angles are 120°, as shown in Fig. 9–1. This suggests that each carbon atom is sp^2 hybridized. By allowing the three sp^2 hybrid orbitals containing one electron each to overlap two sp^2 hybrid orbitals from carbon and one 1*s* orbital from hydrogen, each carbon forms three σ bonds, one with a hydrogen atom and two with two carbon neighbors. The fourth electron occupies a *p* orbital whose two lobes are above and below the plane of the ring, Fig. 9–2*a*. But since there are six of these orbitals, all parallel to each other, each of them overlaps not just one neighbor, as in ethylene, but two neighbors and overlaps both of them equally well. This results in what may be viewed as two doughnut-shaped electron clouds lying above and below the plane of the benzene ring. In this manner each electron binds together not just two, but all

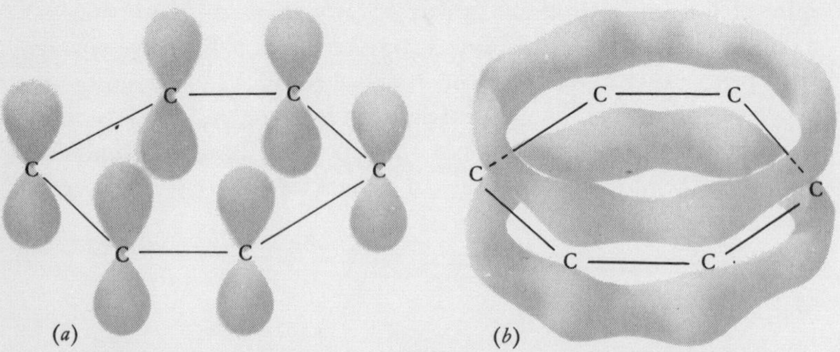

Figure 9–2 Overlap of *p* orbitals in the benzene molecule.

six carbon nuclei of the benzene ring. Instead of the six p electrons being assigned to three π orbitals each of which bonds two specific carbon atoms, they can be assigned to three molecular orbitals (each holding two electrons) which provide for bonding of all six carbon atoms.

9–2 DELOCALIZATION AND DELOCALIZATION ENERGY

The ability of the π electrons of benzene to participate in the formation of more than one bond is frequently referred to as delocalization. Delocalization of π electrons results in the formation of bonds which are stronger than ordinary covalent bonds between two atoms. The stronger the bond, the more energy has been liberated in forming it, and the molecule as a whole is therefore more stable than we have reason to expect on the basis of its conventional formula, which recognizes covalent bonds between two atoms only.

The extra stabilization thus bestowed on a molecule in which electron delocalization is possible is called the delocalization energy. In the case of C_6H_6, it is the difference between the calculable energy of cyclohexatriene, a hypothetical olefinic molecule containing six alternating single and double bonds, and the actual energy of benzene, whose carbon atoms are held together by six equal bonds of the type discussed in the preceding section.

9–3 REPRESENTATION OF BENZENE—RESONANCE

We shall represent the delocalization of π electrons in the benzene ring by the symbol VI. The hexagon indicates the skeleton of six carbon atoms, and the broken circle indicates the π-electron cloud of six electrons.

VI

For another representation of benzene, we must call upon the concept of resonance. This is a second way of arriving at an understanding of these properties of organic molecules not readily expressed by conventional structures. The following principles are a brief outline of the resonance concept:

1. Whenever a molecule can be represented by two or more structures which differ from each other only in the distribution of valence electrons, and not in the distribution of atomic nuclei, resonance is said to occur. Thus the usual structure for formaldehyde is VIIa, but it is also possible to represent the structure as VIIb:

$$\underset{\text{VIIa}}{H_2C{=}\ddot{O}\!:}\qquad\qquad \underset{\text{VIIb}}{H_2\overset{+}{C}{-}\ddot{\underset{..}{O}}\!:^{-}}$$

When resonance occurs, the molecule cannot be represented adequately by any of these structures and is said to be a resonance hybrid. The several structures are said to contribute to the hybrid. In our illustration, formaldehyde is said to be a hybrid of VIIb and VIIb and both structures contribute to the resonance hybrid.

Similarly, benzene can be represented by structures VIIIa and VIIIb, which differ from each other only in the arrangement of electrons and not in the arrangement of atomic nuclei. Benzene is thus a resonance hybrid of VIIIa and VIIIb.

VIIIa VIIIb

2. When the structures which contribute to the resonance hybrid are of about equal stability, resonance is important. But if there are unequal contributing structures, that of lowest energy (highest stability) will most nearly represent the actual structure of the molecule.

VIIa and VIIb are obviously two unequal contributing structures. Hence, resonance should not be as important as in benzene, where the two structures VIIIa and VIIIb are indistinguishable save for a 60° rotation in the plane of the paper. We might also conclude that VIIa is of lower energy, and hence more stable, than VIIb, because the separation of charges leading to VIIb requires energy. Principle 2 states that structure VIIa represents the actual state of formaldehyde better than VIIb does. On the other hand, VIIIa and VIIIb make equal contributions to the hybrid, and the actual state of benzene cannot be adequately represented by either VIIIa or VIIIb.

3. The resonance hybrid is more stable than any of the contributing structures. The increase in stability is called the resonance energy and corresponds to the delocalization energy discussed in the preceding section. The more nearly alike the contributing, or resonance, structures, the greater the resonance energy. For formaldehyde the contributing structures VIIa and VIIb are unequal and the resonance energy is relatively small. For benzene the contributing structures VIIIa and VIIIb are equal and the resonance energy is relatively large.

9-4 OTHER AROMATIC SUBSTANCES

Delocalization or resonance in the case of planar cyclic molecules gives rise to the properties commonly associated with aromatic character: a tendency to undergo electrophilic substitution rather than addition and unusual stability toward oxidizing and reducing agents. Some other important aromatic substances are illustrated in formulas IX to XV. It has been found that aromatic

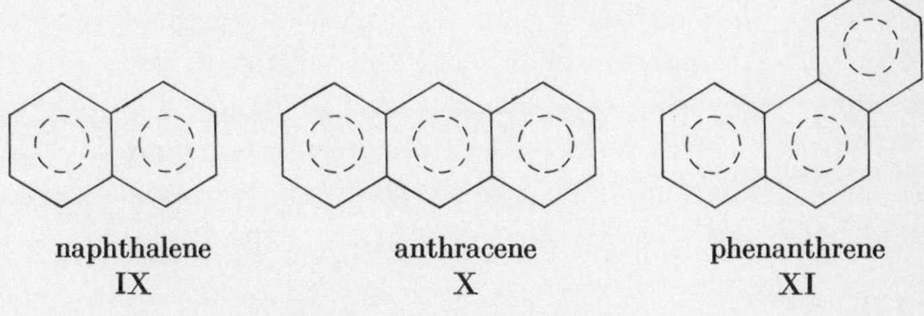

naphthalene IX — anthracene X — phenanthrene XI

Some heterocyclic compounds

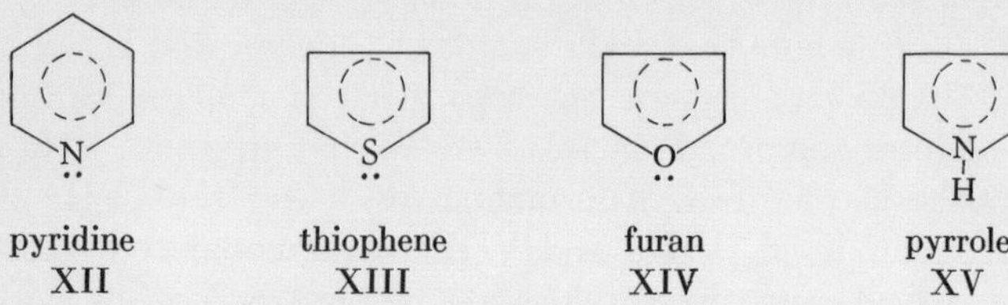

pyridine XII | thiophene XIII | furan XIV | pyrrole XV

character is associated with the delocalization of $(4n + 2)$ π electrons in a planar cyclic substance, where $n = 1, 2, 3, \ldots$. A count of π electrons and of electrons in filled p orbitals which can overlap also will show that the above compounds all fit this definition.

9–5 DELOCALIZATION IN DIENES—1,3-BUTADIENE

Although π-electron delocalization is most pronounced in planar cyclic substances where the conditions for p-orbital overlap are most favorable, it is by no means limited to such compounds. Consider, for example, the molecule 1,3-butadiene (XVI). Free rotation can occur about the central carbon-carbon single bond,

$$CH_2{=}CH{-}CH{=}CH_2$$
XVI

and many different conformations are possible. However, only in the two conformations that are illustrated in Fig. 9–3 are all four p orbitals parallel. When the molecule assumes these shapes, the two central p orbitals overlap not only the two p orbitals at the end of the chain, but also each other. As we have seen, this means that all four π electrons of butadiene interact with each other and are somewhat delocalized. We would therefore expect 1,3-butadiene to be somewhat more stable—i.e., its energy to be somewhat less—than a (hypothetical) substance containing one single carbon-carbon bond and two double bonds whose π electrons do not interact.

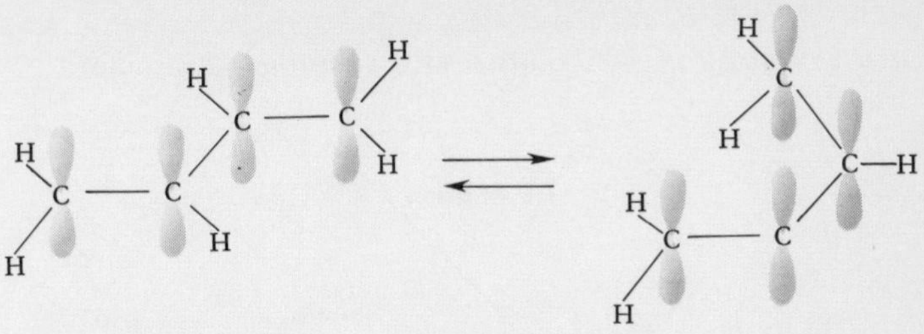

Figure 9–3 Stable conformations of 1,3-butadiene.

Using the resonance concept, butadiene may be represented by the contributing structures XVIIa, b, and c. In accordance with principle 1 (page 98), these differ from each other only in

$$\overset{+}{C}H_2\text{—}CH\text{=}CH\text{—}\overset{-}{C}H_2 \leftrightarrow CH_2\text{=}CH\text{—}CH\text{=}CH_2 \leftrightarrow \overset{-}{C}H_2\text{—}CH\text{=}CH\text{—}\overset{+}{C}H_2$$

XVIIa XVIIb XVIIc

the distribution of electrons, not in the arrangement of atomic nuclei. Hence resonance may be invoked. The double arrows indicate that neither XVIIa, XVIIb, nor XVIIc adequately represents the actual state of the butadiene molecule. Although XVIIa and XVIIc are equivalent, they differ from XVIIb and might be expected to be somewhat less stable than XVIIb because of the separation of charge. In accordance with principle 2 (p. 98), then, XVIIb will most nearly represent the actual structure of the butadiene molecule.

Evidence for Delocalization in 1,3-Butadiene

The chemical behavior of 1,3-butadiene is indeed sufficiently different from that of ordinary alkenes to have suggested, long before resonance or molecular orbital theory was developed, some kind of interaction between the carbon atoms at the end of the chain. For example, the addition of one molecule of bromine results not only in the formation of the expected 1,2-dibromo-3-butene but also in the formation of 1,4-dibromo-2-butene:

$$CH_2{=}CH{-}CH{=}CH_2 + Br_2 \xrightarrow{\text{1,2 addition}} \underset{Br}{\underset{|}{CH_2}}{-}\underset{Br}{\underset{|}{CH}}{-}CH{=}CH_2 \qquad (8)$$

$$CH_2{=}CH{-}CH{=}CH_2 + Br_2 \xrightarrow{\text{1,4 addition}} \underset{Br}{\underset{|}{CH_2}}{-}CH{=}CH{-}\underset{Br}{\underset{|}{CH_2}}$$

Again, the absorption of ultraviolet light, a property characteristic of molecules containing π electrons, is not that of an ordinary alkene, but indicates what has been called conjugation between the double bonds. This delocalization of the π electrons, or resonance, in butadiene is sometimes represented by formulas containing fractional bonds, such as XVIII. But while X-ray and electron diffraction measurements show that the carbon-carbon bond distances in butadiene are not quite those of normal

$$CH_2{\overset{--}{=}}CH{\overset{--}{=}}CH{\overset{--}{=}}CH_2$$

XVIII

double and single bonds, they also prove that the three carbon-carbon bonds are not equivalent, although their equivalence might be inferred from a representation such as XVIII.

It is not necessary that the two interacting π-electron systems belong to two double bonds as in 1,3-butadiene or its homologs. The reactions and spectroscopic properties of compounds XIX and XX, where the double bond of a carbonyl group is conjugated[1] with a double bond, have long been interpreted as

[1] The term "conjugated" used in this sense means that the two double bonds are separated by one single bond.

indicating an interaction between the carbon atoms at the end of the conjugated system which can be explained in terms of electron delocalization.

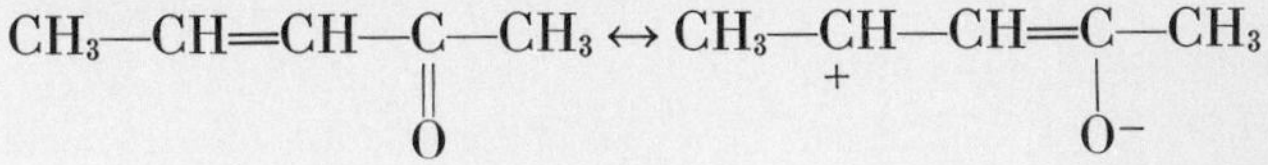

$$CH_3\text{—}CH\text{=}CH\text{—}\underset{\underset{O}{\|}}{C}\text{—}CH_3 \leftrightarrow CH_3\text{—}\overset{}{\underset{+}{C}H}\text{—}CH\text{=}\underset{\underset{O^-}{|}}{C}\text{—}CH_3$$

XIX

$$CH_2\text{=}CH\text{—}\underset{\underset{O}{\|}}{C}\text{—}OH \leftrightarrow \underset{+}{C}H_2\text{—}CH\text{=}\underset{\underset{O^-}{|}}{C}\text{—}OH$$

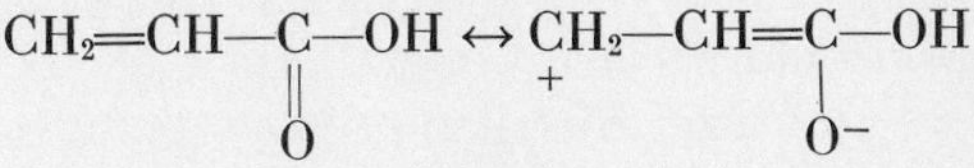

XX

9-6 THE ACETATE ION

The acetate ion, $CH_3CO_2^-$, furnishes us with another example of electron delocalization or resonance. The conventional structure XXIa indicates that the sp^2-hybridized carboxyl carbon is

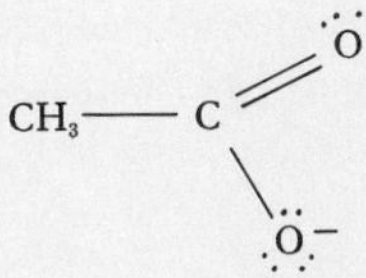

XXIa 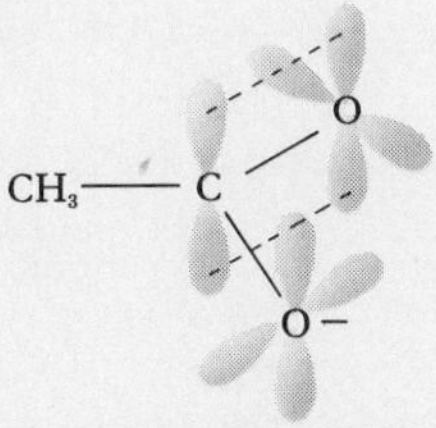 XXIb 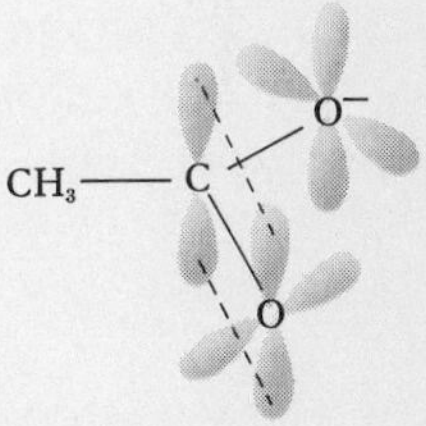 XXIc

linked to the carbonyl oxygen by a σ bond and a π bond, the π bond resulting from overlap between a half-filled p orbital of carbon and a half-filled p orbital of oxygen. The third p orbital of the carbonyl oxygen contains two electrons, an unshared electron pair. The formula also indicates that carbon is linked by a σ bond to the negatively charged oxygen whose remaining two p orbitals are filled by two unshared electron pairs.

But because the three atoms involved all lie in one plane and because of the symmetry properties of the carboxylate ion, formulas XXIb and XXIc are entirely equivalent. This means that the *p* orbital of carbon can overlap a *p* orbital of either oxygen equally well. Thus four electrons, one contributed by carbon and three contributed by the two oxygens, are delocalized and occupy new molecular orbitals which bind the three atoms together. In the terms of resonance theory, the acetate ion is a resonance hybrid of two structures XXIIa and XXIIb which, being entirely equivalent, contribute equally to the actual state

$$\underset{\text{XXIIa}}{CH_3\text{—}C\overset{\large /\!\!/ O}{\underset{\large \backslash O^-}{}}} \quad \longleftrightarrow \quad \underset{\text{XXIIb}}{CH_3\text{—}C\overset{\large / O^-}{\underset{\large \backslash\!\!\backslash O}{}}} \quad \text{or} \quad \underset{\text{XXIIc}}{\left\{ CH_3\text{—}C\overset{\large /\!\!/\!\!/ O}{\underset{\large \backslash\!\!\backslash\!\!\backslash O}{}} \right\}^-}$$

of the molecule. This actual state might perhaps be represented by formula XXIIc, which indicates that the negative charge is distributed over both oxygens and that the two carbon-oxygen bonds are equivalent. This conclusion is confirmed by X-ray and electron diffraction measurements which show that the carboxylate ion is planar and that the two carbon-oxygen bonds are of equal length.

9–7 ACIDITY OF CARBOXYLIC ACIDS AND ALCOHOLS

The above argument applies not only to the acetate ion but also to the anions of all carboxylic acids. In this connection we might inquire why the —OH group of a carboxylic acid is so much more acidic than the —OH group of an alcohol. Acidity here implies the transfer of a proton to a base, most generally water, whose extent is measured by the equilibrium constants of the two reactions

$$R\text{—}OH + H_2O \rightleftharpoons R\text{—}O^- + H_3O^+ \qquad K_A = 10^{-16}, \text{ approx.} \tag{9}$$

$$R\text{—}CO_2H + H_2O \rightleftharpoons R\text{—}CO_2^- + H_3O^+ \qquad K_A = 10^{-5}, \text{ approx.} \tag{10}$$

We see that carboxylic acids are one hundred billion times stronger acids than alcohols are.

In the first equilibrium, Eq. (9), electron delocalization is a factor neither in the alcohol molecule nor in the anion derived from it. On the other hand, we can write resonance structures for the undissociated acid (XXIII) as well as for the carboxylate ion (XXIV).

$$\underset{\text{XXIIIa}}{R\text{—}C(=O)\text{—}OH} \leftrightarrow \underset{\text{XXIIIb}}{R\text{—}C(\text{—}O^-)=\overset{+}{O}H} \underset{+H^+}{\overset{-H^+}{\rightleftharpoons}} \underset{\text{XXIVa}}{R\text{—}C(=O)\text{—}O^-} \leftrightarrow \underset{\text{XXIVb}}{R\text{—}C(\text{—}O^-)=O} \tag{11}$$

The structures on the left of Eq. (11) imply overlap of the filled but unshared *p* orbital on the hydroxyl oxygen with the π orbitals of the carbonyl group. But these structures are not equivalent, and the delocalization energy is relatively low. Conversely, the structures contributing to the resonance hybrid on the right (XXIVa and XXIVb) are equivalent; hence, the delocalization energy in the carboxylate anion is relatively high. Consequently, although both acid and anion are stabilized by resonance, stabilization is much greater for the anion than for the acid and equilibrium (10) lies farther to the right than equilibrium (9).

9-8 SUMMARY

Benzene, C_6H_6, is the simplest representative of the class of aromatic hydrocarbons. The empirical formula of benzene suggests the presence of double bonds; but unlike alkene, benzene does not readily undergo addition reactions. Instead, the typical reactions of benzene involve substitution of one or more hydrogen atoms.

One mono and three disubstitution products can be obtained. The chemical and physical evidence indicates that benzene is a flat symmetrical cyclic molecule having six equivalent carbon-carbon and six equivalent carbon-hydrogen bonds.

The shape and chemical stability of benzene and other aromatic hydrocarbons can be rationalized in terms of two concepts: (1) delocalization of π electrons or (2) resonance.

These concepts can also be used to explain the physical and chemical properties of other molecules containing two or more pairs of π electrons or unshared electron pairs.

PROBLEMS

1. Write complete equations for reactions (1) through (6).

2. ΔH for reaction 7 is -50 kcal/mole. Using the table of bond energies given on p. 58, calculate the approximate delocalization (resonance) energy of benzene.

3. Write all structures that in your opinion contribute to the actual structure of CO_3^{2-}, NO_2^-, $CH_3{-}NO_2$ (nitromethane), $CH_3{-}ONO$ (methyl nitrite), $CH_2{=}CH{-}\overset{\overset{\large H}{|}}{C}{=}O$ (acrolein), $NH_2{-}\underset{\underset{^+NH_2}{\|}}{C}{-}NH_2$ (guanidinium ion).

4. Suggest an explanation for the observation that the equilibrium

$$C_6H_5OH + H_2O \rightleftharpoons C_6H_5O^- + H_3O^+$$

lies farther to the right than equilibrium (9).

X

Making and Breaking Bonds—Aromatic Substitution

It will now be possible to contrast the course of a typical aromatic substitution reaction, say, the reaction of benzene and bromine in the presence of a small amount of ferric bromide, with the addition reaction of a typical olefin.

10–1 MECHANISM OF AROMATIC SUBSTITUTION REACTIONS

In the case of propylene, the somewhat simplified mechanism discussed on pages 83–84 invokes polarization of the bromine molecule by the π-electron cloud of the alkene, Eq. (1). This results in the formation of the most stable carbonium ion, which then reacts with bromide ion to form product, Eq. (2).

$$CH_3CH{=}CH_2 + \overset{\delta+}{Br} - \overset{\delta-}{Br} \rightarrow CH_3\overset{+}{C}H{-}CH_2Br + Br^- \quad (1)$$

$$CH_3\overset{+}{C}H{-}CH_2Br + Br^- \rightarrow CH_3\underset{\substack{|\\Br}}{C}HCH_2Br \quad (2)$$

The more stable π-electron system of an aromatic substance seems to be unable to polarize the halogen molecules sufficiently to promote addition. It is the function of ferric bromide to bring this about in the first step, Eq. (3), either by complete ionization

$$FeBr_3 + Br_2 \rightarrow FeBr_4^- + Br^+ \qquad (3)$$

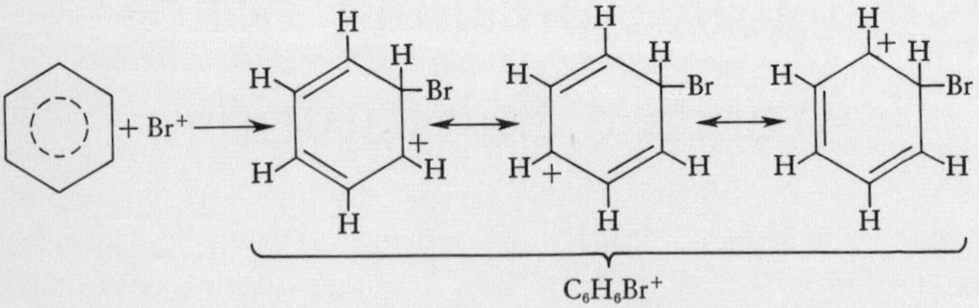

$$+ Br^+ \longrightarrow \quad \longleftrightarrow \quad \longleftrightarrow \qquad (4)$$

$C_6H_6Br^+$

$$C_6H_6Br^+ + FeBr_4^- \rightarrow \quad + HBr + FeBr_3 \qquad (5)$$

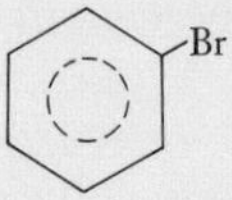

as indicated or by polarization. In the second step Eq. (4), the electrophilic bromide ion attaches itself to one of the carbon atoms of the benzene ring. Now, in the resulting carbonium ion the positive charge is not localized on one carbon atom but distributed over the whole molecule. The three structures shown on the right of Eq. (4) differ from each other only in the distribution of electrons and contribute importantly to the actual state of the ion, which is a hybrid. Although the ion is of higher energy, i.e., less stable, than the original benzene molecule, the dispersal of charge makes it more stable than one of the contributing structures.

It will not be necessary to describe in detail the transition state of reaction 4, i.e., the transition state leading from benzene and Br^+ to $C_6H_6Br^+$. However, it can be seen that it will contain a developing positive charge which, like the positive charge of $C_6H_6Br^+$, will be dispersed over the whole molecule. Hence, the energy required to form the transition state leading to $C_6H_6Br^+$ is less than if the developing positive charge were localized on one carbon atom.

The chief difference between the reactions of propylene and benzene, however, lies in the fate of the carbonium ion. The preferred mode of reaction of the ion $C_6H_6Br^+$ is not addition of Br^- but loss of a proton to $FeBr_4^-$, Eq. (5). This regenerates the aromatic system of six π electrons with its high stability due to electron delocalization.

The other substitution reactions of benzene are thought to involve attack by other electrophiles. Generally, these are positively charged species: nitration, the nitronium ion NO_2^+; sulfonation, probably sulfur trioxide; alkylation, a carbonium ion generated by action of aluminum chloride on the alkyl halide; and acylation, an "acylium" ion R—C$^+$=O produced by action of aluminum chloride on an acid chloride.

10-2 DIRECTING EFFECTS IN AROMATIC SUBSTITUTION

One feature of the proposed mechanism of aromatic substitution is of considerable importance. It deals with the so-called directing effect of groups already attached to the aromatic nucleus on the position of a new entering group. A few examples will make this clear.

Nitration of toluene

$$C_6H_5CH_3 + HNO_3 \xrightarrow{H_2SO_4} o\text{-}CH_3C_6H_4NO_2 + p\text{-}CH_3C_6H_4NO_2 \qquad (6)$$

toluene — *o*-nitrotoluene — *p*-nitrotoluene

Bromination of anisole

$$\text{anisole} + Br_2 \rightarrow \textit{o}\text{-bromoanisole} + \textit{p}\text{-bromoanisole} \qquad (7)$$

OCH_3 OCH_3, Br OCH_3, Br

anisole   *o*-bromo-anisole   *p*-bromo-anisole

Chlorination of nitrobenzene

$$\text{nitrobenzene} + Cl_2 \xrightarrow{FeCl_3} \textit{m}\text{-chloronitrobenzene} \qquad (8)$$

NO_2 NO_2, Cl

nitrobenzene   *m*-chloronitro-benzene

It will be noted that the nitration of toluene and the bromination of anisole result in the formation of two of the three possible isomers, the so-called *ortho* and *para* isomers. A relatively insignificant amount of the *meta* isomer is formed also. Substitution reactions on nitrobenzene, however, yield mainly the meta isomer. The methyl and methoxy radicals are ortho- and para-directing groups; the nitro group is an example of a meta-directing group.

The effect of these and other groups on the direction and velocity of aromatic substitution reactions can be understood if we consider the effect on the stability of the carbonium ion postulated to be the intermediate in electrophilic aromatic substitution and on the energy of the transition state leading to that ion.

10–3 THE NITRATION OF ANISOLE

We shall consider two very simple cases to illustrate the point made in the preceding paragraph. First, let us look at the nitration of anisole, which is depicted in Eq. (9). The product is mainly *p*-nitroanisole accompanied by some *o*-nitroanisole, and there is little, if any, *m*-nitroanisole. Also, the reaction proceeds very readily, much more readily in fact, than the nitration of benzene.

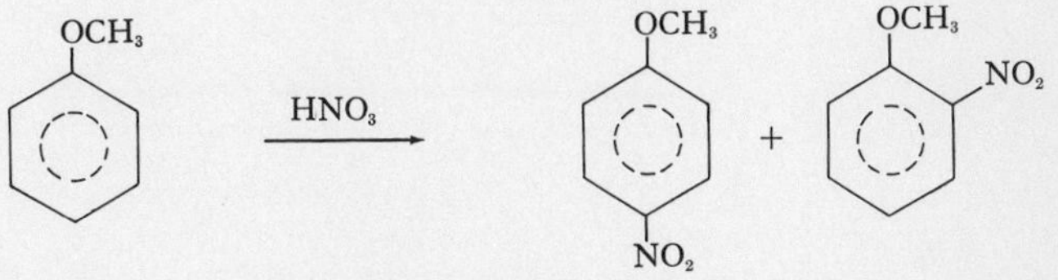

OCH_3 $\xrightarrow{HNO_3}$ OCH_3, NO_2 + OCH_3, NO_2 (9)

We can rephrase these statements as follows: The rate of nitration of anisole is much greater than that of benzene, and the rate of ortho and para substitution is much greater than that of meta substitution. This means that the activation energy for nitration of anisole is less than that of benzene and that the transition states for *ortho* and *para* substitution have lower energies than the transition state for *meta* substitution.

To explain these observations, let us look at the effect exerted by the $—OCH_3$ group on the transition states of the nitration reaction.[1]

For benzene

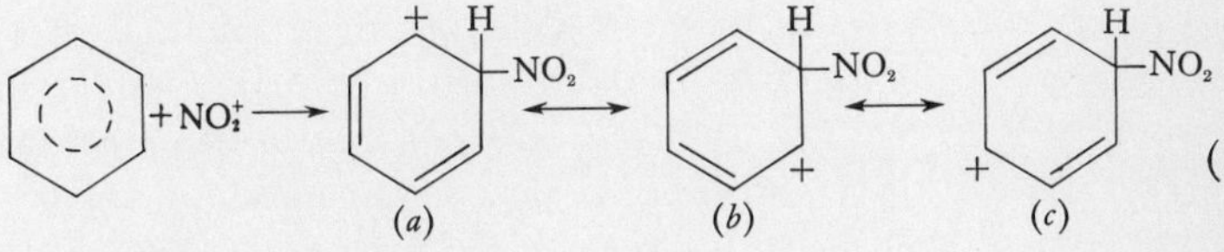

$+ NO_2^+ \longrightarrow$ H, NO_2, + (*a*) $\longleftrightarrow$ H, NO_2, + (*b*) $\longleftrightarrow$ H, NO_2, + (*c*) (10)

I

[1] As was shown on pp. 109–110, resonance hybrids on the right of Eqs. (10) to (13) are not transition states, but carbonium ion intermediates. However, the transition state with its developing positive charge on the ring resembles the intermediate sufficiently closely that its stabilization can be discussed in terms of the stabilization of the intermediate carbonium ion.

For ortho substitution of anisole

$$C_6H_5OCH_3 + NO_2^+ \longrightarrow \underbrace{(a) \longleftrightarrow (b) \longleftrightarrow (c) \longleftrightarrow (d)}_{\text{II}} \quad (11)$$

For para substitution of anisole

$$C_6H_5OCH_3 + NO_2^+ \longrightarrow \underbrace{\ \longleftrightarrow\ \longleftrightarrow\ \longleftrightarrow\ }_{\text{III}} \quad (12)$$

For meta substitution of anisole

$$C_6H_5OCH_3 + NO_2^+ \longrightarrow \underbrace{\ \longleftrightarrow\ \longleftrightarrow\ }_{\text{IV}} \quad (13)$$

Structures IIa, IIb, and IIc, and formulas IIIa, IIIb, and IIIc correspond to the three structures Ia, Ib, and Ic which help to stabilize the intermediate carbonium ion and, by implication (see footnote page 111), the transition state of benzene nitration. But structures IId and IIId, in which the positive charge on carbon is transferred to oxygen as in

$$\overset{+}{\underset{/}{\overset{\diagdown}{C}}}-\ddot{\underset{\cdot\cdot}{O}}-CH_3 \leftrightarrow \underset{/}{\overset{\diagdown}{C}}=\underset{+}{\ddot{O}}-CH_3$$

are new. The number of structures contributing to the resonance hybrids II and III is greater than that contributing to I; hence, by implication, the resonance stabilization of the transition state leading to II and III is greater than the resonance stabilization of the transition state leading to I. The rate of nitration of anisole should, therefore, be greater than that of benzene.

Similarly, if we inspect Eq. (13), we see that meta substitution of anisole goes through a transition state which includes only three contributing resonance structures, none of which involves participation by the methoxyl group. Hence meta substitution of anisole should proceed at a much slower rate than ortho or para substitution.

10-4 THE NITRATION OF NITROBENZENE

The second example is the nitration of nitrobenzene,

$$C_6H_5NO_2 \xrightarrow{HNO_3} m\text{-}C_6H_4(NO_2)_2 \qquad (14)$$

which proceeds with difficulty. More vigorous conditions are required than for the nitration of benzene, and the substitution occurs almost exclusively in the meta position. Since reactions (10) and (14) are so similar, we are justified in assuming that this means that the transition state leading from nitrobenzene to *m*-dinitrobenzene is less stabilized than the transition state leading from benzene to nitrobenzene but more stabilized than the transition states leading to *o*- or *p*-dinitrobenzene.

If we write the reactions leading to intermediates for ortho, meta and para substitution, we obtain the following:

For ortho substitution

$$C_6H_5NO_2 + NO_2^+ \longrightarrow (a) \leftrightarrow (b) \leftrightarrow (c) \qquad (15)$$

V

For para substitution

$$C_6H_5NO_2 + NO_2^+ \longrightarrow (a) \leftrightarrow (b) \leftrightarrow (c) \qquad (16)$$

VI

For meta substitution

$$C_6H_5NO_2 + NO_2^+ \longrightarrow (a) \leftrightarrow (b) \leftrightarrow (c) \qquad (17)$$

VII

Now the nitro group can be represented electronically as follows:

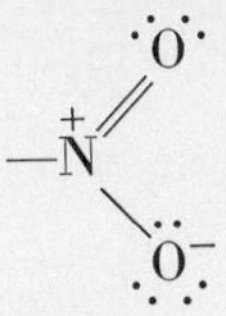

```
      ·Ö·
    +//
   —N
      \
       Ö⁻
       ··
```

This representation shows that the nitrogen atom has a large degree of positive character. Hence structures Vc and VIc, in which the positive nitrogen would be adjacent to another positive charge, are energetically quite unfavorable compared with Va and Vb; VIa and VIb; and VIIa, VIIb and VIIc. The result is that structures resembling Vc and VIc will contribute little to the resonance hybrid of the transition states for ortho and para substitution. Resonance stabilization of the meta transition state with three more or less equivalent contributing structures would be expected to be greater than resonance stabilization of the ortho and para transition states, each possessing only two important contributing structures. Hence the nitration of nitrobenzene will proceed largely to the meta isomer.

That the rate of meta nitration of nitrobenzene should be lower than the rate of nitration of benzene is seen by comparing Eq. (10) with Eq. (17). The nitrogen atom with its positive charge would be expected to destabilize the contributing structures resembling VIIa, VIIb, and VIIc relative to those not containing the extra nitro group, raise the activation energy, and therefore lower the rate.

Similar arguments can be used to explain the effect of other substituent groups on the rate and direction of electrophilic aromatic substitution.

10–5 SUMMARY

The mechanism of aromatic substitution reactions is thought to involve in its first stage the attack of an electrophilic ion on the π-electron system of benzene and its derivatives, and thus to resemble the first stage of additions to olefins. The second stage, however, involves elimination of a proton with regeneration of the resonance-stabilized aromatic system.

The directive effect of groups on further substitution on the benzene ring and their effect on the rate of substitution can be rationalized in terms of this mechanism.

PROBLEMS

1. Write equations analogous to Eqs. (4) and (5) for the reaction of benzene with the carbonium ion $CH_3—\overset{+}{C}H—CH_3$ and the acylium ion $CH_3—CH_2—\overset{+}{C}{=}O$.

2. Suggest an explanation for the following observation:

$$C_6H_6 + CH_3CH_2CH_2Cl \xrightarrow[75°]{AlCl_3} C_6H_5—CH(CH_3)—CH_3$$

3. Predict the product of the reaction of

m-nitroanisole (OCH_3 and $—NO_2$ on benzene ring, meta) and p-nitroanisole (OCH_3 and NO_2 on benzene ring, para)

with bromine in the presence of iron. How do the rates of reaction compare with each other and with the rates of bromination of anisole and nitrobenzene?

4. Predict the products of the nitrations of

C_6H_5CN $\quad$ $C_6H_5CO_2H$ $\quad$ m-$C_6H_4(NO_2)_2$

Compare the rates of nitration with those of benzene.

XI

The Shape of Molecules—Optical Activity

WE SAW IN CHAP. IV that the existence of geometrical isomers is a consequence of the rigidity of double bonds or rings, which prevents interconversion of the isomers, at least under normal conditions. There is, however, another aspect of organic molecules which we have not yet considered and which may give rise to a still different type of isomerism. This aspect deals with the symmetry properties of organic molecules.

11–1 SYMMETRY AND ASYMMETRY

An object is said to have a plane of symmetry if a plane can be passed through it in such a way that the part of the object on one side of the plane is the mirror image of the other (see Fig. 11–1). An object is said to have a center of symmetry if it contains a point within it such that any straight line through that point encounters the same environment in each of its two directions. An object having a plane or center of symmetry is called a symmetric object; an object having neither is called an asymmetric object. A symmetric object is superimposable on its mirror image; an asymmetric object is not—in the same way that our left and right hands are not superimposable (see Fig. 11–2).

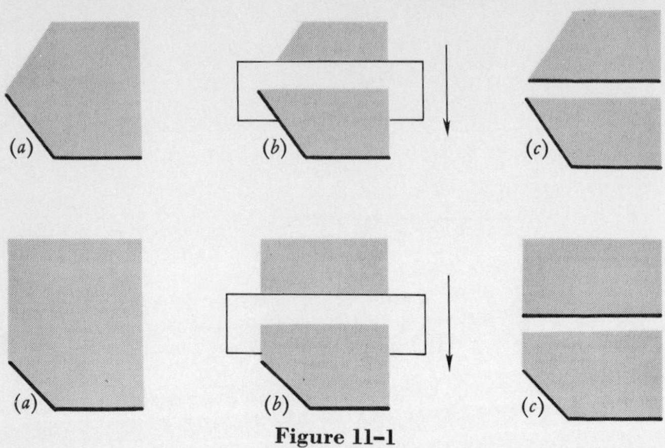

Figure 11–1

11–2 ENANTIOMERIC MOLECULES

Molecules, like any other objects, may be symmetric or asymmetric. An asymmetric molecule will not be superimposable on its mirror image. In deciding whether a molecule is asymmetric or not, we must always assume that free rotation about the single bonds is possible, unless it can be clearly shown that certain features prevent it and impose rigidity on the system. If asymmetry is present, the molecule and its mirror image are said to be enantiomers.

We shall be concerned here only with the most common kind of molecular asymmetry, which comes about in the following way. Consider the molecule 2-butanol (I). It can be thought of as a derivative of methane in which the central carbon atom is linked

$$\begin{array}{c} \mathrm{H} \\ | \\ \mathrm{CH_3{—}C{—}CH_2CH_3} \\ | \\ \mathrm{OH} \end{array}$$

2-butanol

I

to four different groups: $—H$, $—OH$, $—CH_3$, and $—CH_2CH_3$. Let us now construct a model of 2-butanol by attaching these

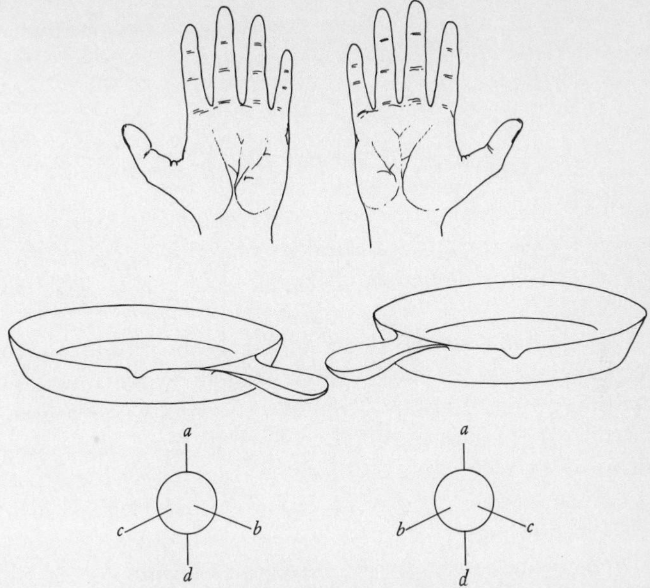

Figure 11–2 Nonidentical mirror images.

four groups to the central carbon atom as we would the four hydrogens of methane. We find that not one but two arrangements (II and III) are possible, the two models being mirror images of each other. Each model represents one of the two enantiomers of 2-butanol. The asymmetry of 2-butanol is due

CH_2CH_3
HO H
CH_3
II

CH_2CH_3
H OH
CH_3
III

to the presence of the central carbon atom, which carries four different substituents. Such carbon atoms are called *asymmetric carbon atoms.* When we see that a certain formula contains an asymmetric carbon atom, we should recognize the possible existence of enantiomers.[1]

11-3 ROTATION OF POLARIZED LIGHT

Although enantiomers are different compounds, their physical properties are the same unless they are placed in an asymmetrical environment. To distiguish between them, we use plane-polarized light.

Ordinary light can be thought of as a wavefront in which vibrations occur in all planes perpendicular to the direction of propagation. Figure 11–3*a* shows the vibrations which occur if we look directly at a beam of light. Each of these vibrations can be imagined as being the resultant of two vibrations at right angles to one another. Figure 11–3*b* shows this schematically for one of the vibrations.

A light beam can be passed through certain materials which have the property of adsorbing or selectively refracting one of these two components. The emerging light beam vibrates only in the plane of the unadsorbed or unrefracted component and is said to be "plane-polarized."

When a beam of plane-polarized light is passed through one of the enantiomers of 2-butanol, the plane of the emerging beam is different from the plane of the entering beam. We say that the

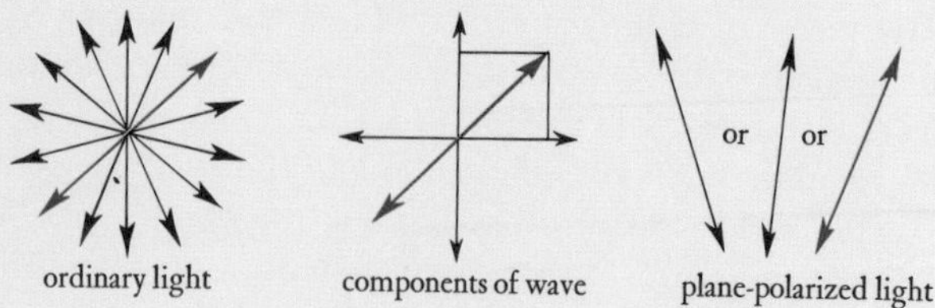

Figure 11–3 Propagation of light.

[1] Strictly speaking, the presence of an asymmetric carbon atom is neither a necessary nor a sufficient condition for asymmetry, since asymmetry depends on the shape and rigidity of the molecule as a whole.

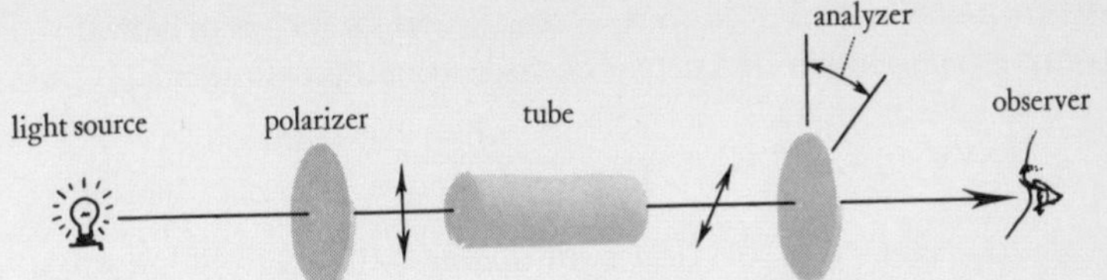

Figure 11–4 Schematic representation of a polarimeter.

plane of the polarized light has been *rotated* and that the substance, in this case 2-butanol, is *optically active.*

The rotation of the plane of plane-polarized light is measured by means of an instrument called a polarimeter, which is represented schematically in Fig. 11–4. Light from a light source passes through a lens called the polarizer, through a tube containing the optically active substance, through a second lens called the analyzer, and finally reaches the observer. The two lenses are made of materials which selectively refract one of the two components of the vibrations in a light beam.

Let us assume that the tube is empty. Then a maximum amount of light will reach the observer when the lenses are arranged to pass light vibrating in the same plane. When the analyzer is rotated, less and less light will come through. When the analyzer is at right angles to its original position, the amount of light transmitted will be at a minimum.

If an optically active sample is now placed in the tube, it will rotate the plane of polarized light. Then the analyzer will have to be turned through a certain angle of rotation in order to reduce the transmitted light to a minimum again. The angle of rotation can be measured by a circular scale. If the analyzer has to be turned to the right, the substance is dextrorotatory, or +; if the analyzer has to be turned to the left, the substance is levorotatory, or −.

The angle of rotation is characteristic of the asymmetric substance, but it also depends on concentration (the number of asymmetric molecules which the beam encounters), the wavelength of the plane-polarized light used, the temperature, and the solvent.

The angle of rotation is usually expressed in terms of the specific rotation, which is defined by the following equation:

$$\text{specific rotation } [\alpha] = \frac{\text{observed rotation}}{\text{length of sample} \times \text{concentration}}$$

where the observed rotation is in degrees, the sample length is in decimeters, and the concentration is in grams per milliliter. We find that the two forms of 2-butanol have a specific rotation equal in absolute value but opposite in sign. All of their other properties —melting points, boiling points, densities, and solubilities in various solvents—are the same.

11–4 RACEMATES

To distinguish them by the sign of their specific rotation, the two forms of 2-butanol are generally referred to as (+)-2-butanol and (−)-2-butanol. When equal amounts of both isomers are mixed, the rotation caused by the molecules of the (+)-isomer is counterbalanced by the rotation of the molecules of the (−)-isomer and the mixture as a whole is optically inactive. Such a mixture of equal amounts of enantiomers is called a racemate. The physical properties of racemates generally differ from those of the pure + and − isomers, just as we would expect mixtures of *n*-propyl alcohol and isopropyl alcohol to exhibit properties that are different from those of the components.

A substance which has one asymmetric center thus exists in two optically active forms—the two enantiomers—which differ from each other only in the sign of rotation, and one inactive form, the racemate, which is a mixture of equal amounts of the enantiomers.

11–5 STEREOMERS OF 2,3-DIHYDROXYBUTYRIC ACID

Substances which have the same gross structure but differ from each other in configuration are frequently called stereoisomers or stereomers. The study of stereomers is called stereochemistry.

When the number of asymmetric centers per molecule is larger—and many substances elaborated by nature contain two or more asymmetric carbon atoms—the number of possible isomers increases very rapidly and the question of stereochemistry becomes very complex. Let us merely illustrate the problem by discussing the number of stereomers in a simple open-chain molecule containing two asymmetric carbon atoms such as 2,3-dihydroxybutyric acid (IV). (In IV, as in subsequent formulas, centers of asymmetry are starred.)

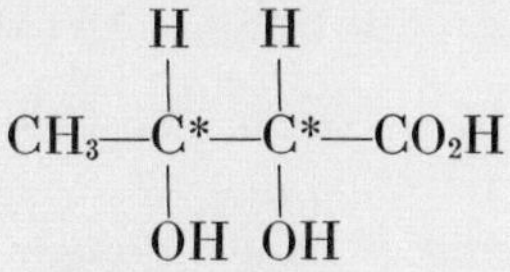

$$\begin{array}{ccccccc} & & H & & H & & \\ & & | & & | & & \\ CH_3 & — & C^* & — & C^* & — & CO_2H \\ & & | & & | & & \\ & & OH & & OH & & \end{array}$$

IV

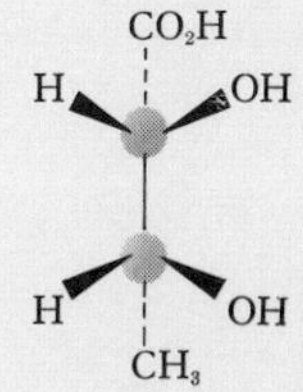

Va: CO_2H; H, OH; H, OH; CH_3

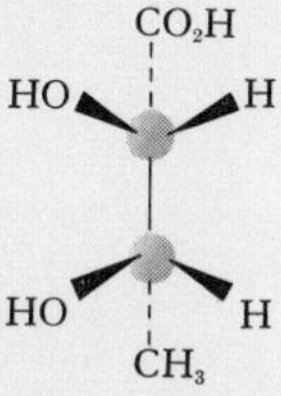

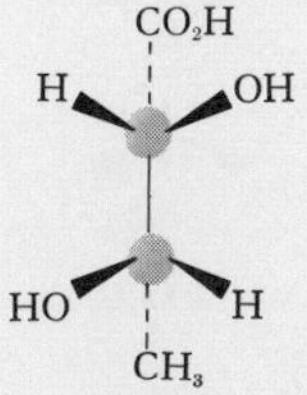

Vb: CO_2H; HO, H; HO, H; CH_3

VIa: CO_2H; H, OH; HO, H; CH_3

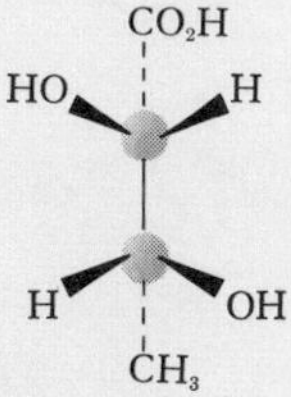

VIb: CO_2H; HO, H; H, OH; CH_3

Formulas Va and Vb and VIa and VIb indicate the four possible configurations of this molecule, all of which are known. Stereomer Vb is the mirror image or enantiomer of Va; the two isomers have equal rotations of opposite sign and, when mixed in equal amounts, produce a racemate. Similarly, Vb is the enantiomer of Va. When mixed in equal amounts, VIa and VIb produce a second racemate. While the specific rotations of Va and Vb are equal, but of opposite sign, the rotations of Va and VIa, or Vb and VIb, bear no obvious relationship to each other. We say that Va and VIa, or Va and VIb, are diastereomers.

Diastereomers are optical isomers which are not mirror images. The physical and chemical properties of enantiomers are the same except for sign of rotation, but the physical and chemical properties of diastereomers differ.

11-6 STEREOMERS OF TARTARIC ACID

Let us now introduce a slight modification in the structure of IV by converting the terminal methyl group to a carboxyl group. The resulting compound is called tartaric acid (VII), and the space formulas corresponding to Va and Vb and VIa and VIb are also tabulated.

$$HO_2C-\overset{\displaystyle H}{\underset{\displaystyle OH}{C^*}}-\overset{\displaystyle H}{\underset{\displaystyle OH}{C^*}}-CO_2H$$

VII

CO_2H / H, OH / H, OH / CO_2H — VIIIa

CO_2H / HO, H / HO, H / CO_2H — VIIIb

*meso*tartaric acid
mp 140°

CO_2H / H, OH / HO, H / CO_2H — IXa

CO_2H / HO, H / H, OH / CO_2H — IXb

(+)-tartaric acid (−)-tartaric acid
mp 170°, +12° mp 170°, −12°
racemic (±)-tartaric acid
mp 206°

Formulas IXa and IXb represent a pair of enantiomers, (+)- and (−)-tartaric acid. When IXa and IXb are mixed in equal amounts, a racemate, racemic (±)-tartaric acid, is produced.

If we now look at formulas VIIIa and VIIIb, we see that VIIIb can be produced from VIIIa simply by rotating VIIIa in the plane of the paper by 180°. This means that VIIIa and VIIIb are superimposable and therefore identical. Even though the molecule represented by VIIIa (or VIIIb) has two asymmetric carbon atoms, it has a plane of symmetry which bisects the bond between the asymmetric centers. Such compounds are therefore optically inactive and are said to have the *meso* configuration. The isomer of tartaric acid represented by VIIIa or VIIIb is called *meso*tartaric acid and is a diastereomer of IXa and IXb.

11-7 ASYMMETRIC SYNTHESIS

It would seem to be a simple matter to make optically active compounds in the laboratory. The catalytic reduction of pyruvic acid, which has no asymmetric center and is optically inactive, to lactic acid, which contains one asymmetric carbon atom, provides an excellent example:

$$\underset{\text{pyruvic acid}}{CH_3{-}\underset{\underset{O}{\|}}{C}{-}CO_2H} + H_2 \xrightarrow{\text{catalyst}} \underset{\text{lactic acid}}{CH_3{-}\overset{H}{\underset{\underset{OH}{|}}{C}}{-}CO_2H} \qquad (1)$$

However, the lactic acid prepared in this way is entirely inactive, i.e., it is a racemate. Why is this so? The answer is that hydrogen can approach the carbonyl group from either direction equally well; therefore, equal amounts of the two enantiomers are formed and the product is inactive.

H——H

CH_3, C═O, CO_2H $\xrightarrow{\text{catalyst}}$ CH_3, H, —OH, CO_2H (2)

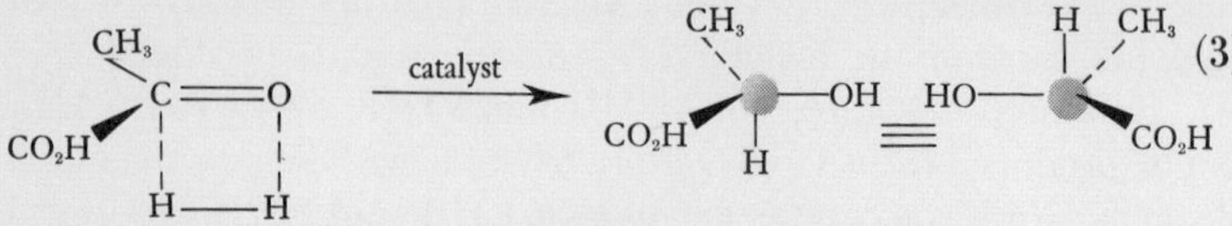

(3)

As another example, consider the preparation of 2-bromobutane by the bromination of *n*-butane in the vapor phase:

$$CH_3CH_2CH_2CH_3 + Br_2 \rightarrow \underset{\displaystyle Br}{\underset{|}{CH_3CH^*}}CH_2CH_3 \qquad (4)$$

The starting material has no asymmetric center. The product has, but it turns out to be a racemate because the two hydrogen atoms being replaced by bromine are equivalent and the probabilities of either being replaced are exactly equal:

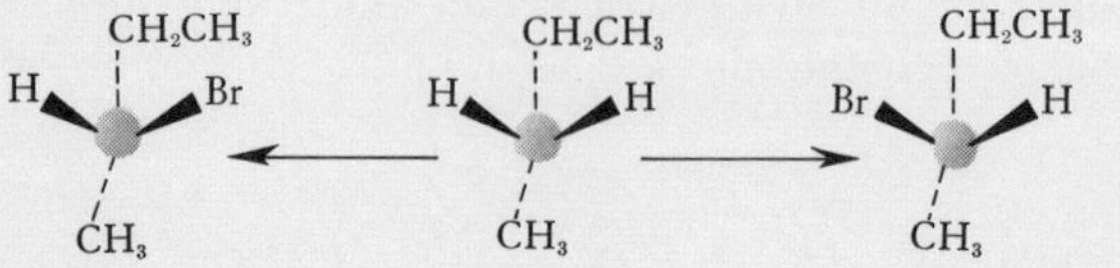

(5)

We conclude that the use of optically inactive reactants always leads to optically inactive products. How is it then possible to prepare optically active substances in the laboratory at all?

Nature provides us with a partial answer to this question. It has been found that organic reactions which occur in plants or animals are catalyzed by complex catalysts, called enzymes, which are themselves asymmetric. As a consequence, the enzymatically catalyzed creation of a new asymmetric center in a biological system—say, the conversion of pyruvic acid to lactic acid—leads to the production of one enantiomer only. Depending on the enzyme system, pyruvic acid may be reduced to either (+)- or (−)-lactic acid. In a quite similar way, a laboratory reaction carried out on an inactive substance in an asymmetric environment or with the use of an asymmetric reagent can lead to the predominant or exclusive formation of one of the two possible isomers.

11-8 RESOLUTION OF RACEMATES

The use of optically active substances provided by nature has led to a method for the separation of racemates into their components. Such a separation of enantiomers, called *resolution*, depends on the formation of diastereomers which, as we have seen earlier, differ in physical properties.

$$\left.\begin{matrix}(+)\text{-RCO}_2\text{H}\\(-)\text{-RCO}_2\text{H}\end{matrix}\right. + (+)\text{-NR}_3' \downarrow$$

racemic acid

$$\underbrace{(+)\text{-RCO}_2^-\ (+)\text{-}\overset{+}{\text{N}}\text{HR}_3' + (-)\text{-R—CO}_2^-\ (+)\text{-}\overset{+}{\text{N}}\text{HR}_3'}_{\text{mixture of diastereomers}}$$

crystallize (6)

$$(+)\text{-RCO}_2^-\ (+)\text{-}\overset{+}{\text{N}}\text{HR}_3' \xrightarrow{\text{HCl}} (+)\text{-RCO}_2\text{H} + (+)\text{-}\overset{+}{\text{N}}\text{HR}_3'\ \text{Cl}^-$$

$$(-)\text{-RCO}_2^-\ (+)\text{-}\overset{+}{\text{N}}\text{HR}_3' \xrightarrow{\text{HCl}} (-)\text{-RCO}_2\text{H} + (+)\text{-}\overset{+}{\text{N}}\text{HR}_3'\ \text{Cl}^-$$

Consider, for example, the separation of a racemic acid into its constituent enantiomers. Assume that we have at our disposal an optically active amine.[1] On mixing the racemate with the amine, we produce a mixture of two salts. One is the salt which the optically active amine forms with the + acid. The second salt is formed from the optically active amine and the − acid. These salts are not mirror images, but diastereomers. Since diastereomers differ in physical properties, the solubilities of the two salts may be sufficiently different to permit separation by fractional crystallization. Once separated, the two salts are treated with mineral acid, a procedure which liberates the optically active acids.

By suitable choice of an optically active resolving agent, almost any racemate can be resolved in this manner.

11–9 ABSOLUTE CONFIGURATION

One more point remains to be clarified. We have seen that models II and III represent the two enantiomers of 2-butanol, (+)-2-butanol, and (−)-2-butanol. But which model represents which isomer? Is the configuration of (−)-2-butanol—the arrangement of atoms in space—that represented by II or III? Is (+)-tartaric acid IXa or IXb?

This question—the question of the absolute configuration of (+)-2-butanol and indeed, the question of the absolute configuration of other simple optically active organic compounds—has been answered only recently. X-ray diffraction experiments showed the configuration of (+)-tartaric acid to be IXa. (−)-Tartaric acid must therefore be IXb and *meso*tartaric acid VIII. This in turn allowed chemists to assign absolute configurations to many compounds which had previously been converted to, or prepared from, one of the tartaric acids. Chart 11–1 illustrates some of these transformations and incidentally shows that III represents the configuration of (−)-2-butanol.

[1] Substances commonly used for this purpose are complex organic amines called alkaloids which can be isolated from plants.

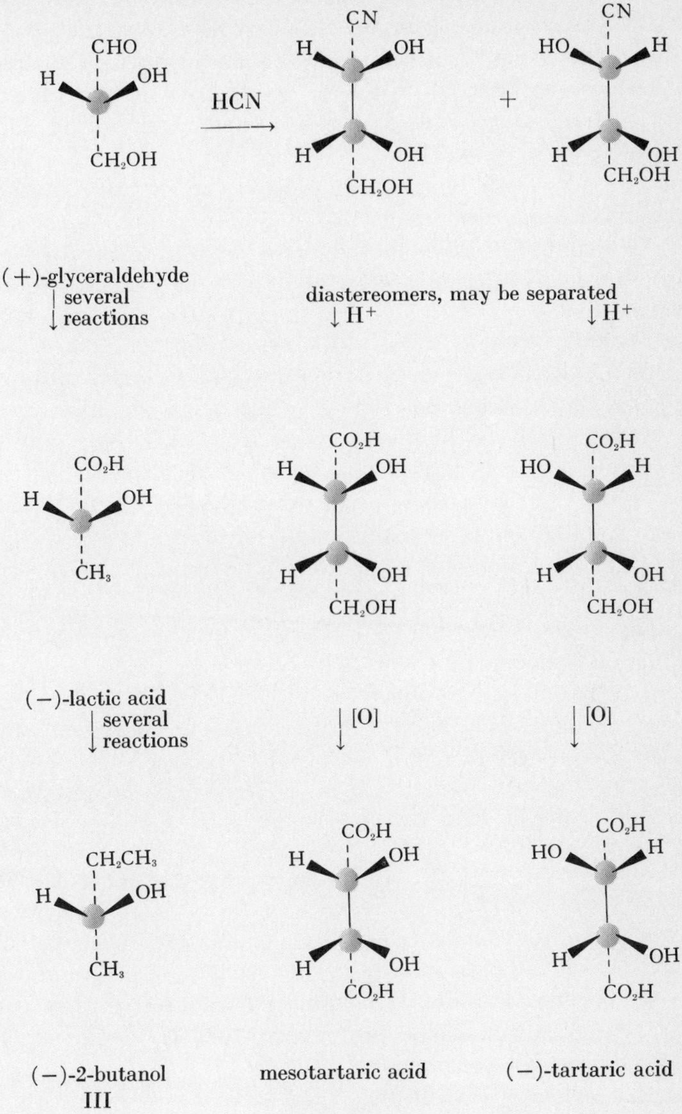

CHO
H OH
CH_2OH

HCN →

CN
H OH
H OH
CH_2OH

\+

CN
HO H
H OH
CH_2OH

(+)-glyceraldehyde
| several
↓ reactions

diastereomers, may be separated
↓ H^+ ↓ H^+

CO_2H
H OH
CH_3

CO_2H
H OH
H OH
CH_2OH

CO_2H
HO H
H OH
CH_2OH

(−)-lactic acid
| several
↓ reactions

| [O]
↓

| [O]
↓

CH_2CH_3
H OH
CH_3

CO_2H
H OH
H OH
CO_2H

CO_2H
HO H
H OH
CO_2H

(−)-2-butanol
III

mesotartaric acid

(−)-tartaric acid

Chart 11-1

It is therefore possible to determine the absolute configuration of any asymmetric center in the most complex of molecules by correlating it with one of the substances whose absolute configuration has been established.

11-10 SUMMARY

Molecular asymmetry leads to the existence of enantiomers—those molecules that are not superimposable on their mirror images.

The most common type of molecular asymmetry arises in compounds which contain carbon atoms carrying four different substituents. Such atoms are called asymmetric carbon atoms.

Enantiomers can be distinguished from each other only by their property of rotating the plane of plane-polarized light in opposite directions, and they are said to be optically active. A mixture of equal amounts of enantiomers, called a racemate, is inactive. The separation of a racemate into its optically active forms is called resolution.

The number of possible optical isomers increases rapidly as the number of asymmetric carbons in a molecule increases. Diastereomers are optical isomers which are not mirror images. The physical and chemical properties of diastereomers are different. This has led to the development of methods for resolution of racemates. Ordinary chemical reactions using inactive starting materials and inactive reagents always lead to racemates, never to optically active compounds.

PROBLEMS

1. Which of the following compounds could exhibit optical ac-

$$CH_3\text{—}CH_2\text{—}\underset{\displaystyle OH}{\underset{|}{CH}}\text{—}CH_2CH_3 \qquad CH_3CH_2\text{—}\overset{\displaystyle CH_3}{\overset{|}{\underset{\displaystyle OH}{\underset{|}{C}}}}\text{—}CH_2CH_2CH_3$$

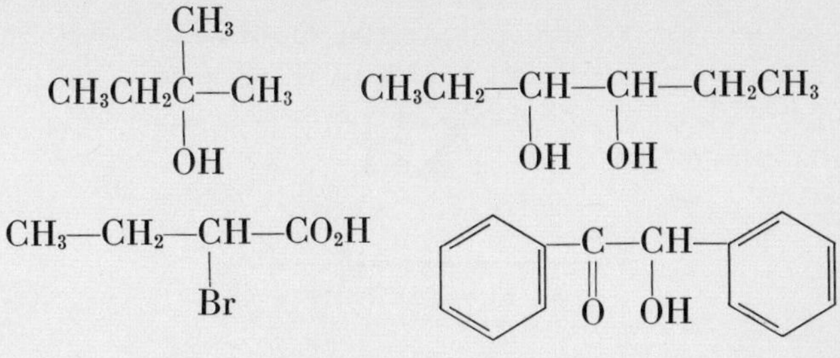

$$\mathrm{CH_3CH_2\overset{\displaystyle CH_3}{\underset{\displaystyle OH}{C}}{-}CH_3} \qquad \mathrm{CH_3CH_2{-}\underset{\displaystyle OH}{CH}{-}\underset{\displaystyle OH}{CH}{-}CH_2CH_3}$$

$$\mathrm{CH_3{-}CH_2{-}\underset{\displaystyle Br}{CH}{-}CO_2H} \qquad \mathrm{C_6H_5{-}\underset{\displaystyle O}{\overset{}{C}}{-}\underset{\displaystyle OH}{CH}{-}C_6H_5}$$

tivity? State how many stereomers are possible for those that do.

2. A substance

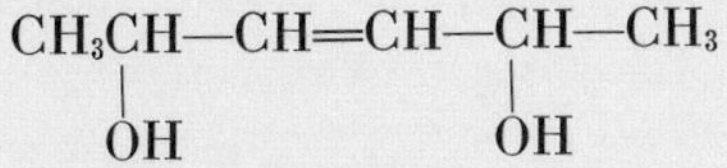

$$\mathrm{CH_3\underset{\displaystyle OH}{CH}{-}CH{=}CH{-}\underset{\displaystyle OH}{CH}{-}CH_3}$$

gives on degradation two molecules of (−) lactic acid per molecule of starting material. Write a structure showing the absolute configuration of the starting material.

3. Write structures for the stereomers of

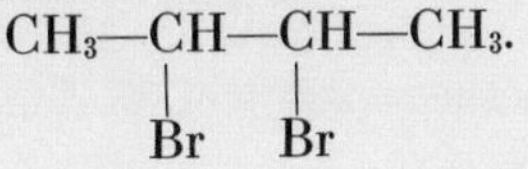

$$\mathrm{CH_3{-}\underset{\displaystyle Br}{CH}{-}\underset{\displaystyle Br}{CH}{-}CH_3}.$$

XII

Conclusion

In the foregoing pages we have attempted to give the reader a brief introduction to that aspect of organic chemistry which deals with the organization of atoms within molecules—structural organic chemistry. Many aspects of this topic were slighted or, of necessity, not even touched upon. Moreover, appreciation of many points requires the sophistication that only further study of organic chemistry can give.

We have tried to point out that the original impetus for the study of organic molecules came from the discovery that organic compounds constitute an important part of our physical environment. The growth in our knowledge of their structure has been most gratifying. Substances whose names everyone knows—sugar, penicillin, chlorophyll, cholesterol—consist of molecules composed of several dozen atoms. Yet our knowledge of their molecular architecture is so exact that we can duplicate them in the laboratory.

The future of organic chemistry is bound up with a more thorough and detailed exploration of our physical and biological environment. More and more complex organic compounds are being isolated and characterized. Some direct and influence biological processes; others have functions which we do not know. Proteins, enzymes, and viruses are beginning to yield the secrets of their construction.

To understand the behavior of these complex substances in biological systems, we must learn more about organic molecules in general. We must learn more about the subtle influences which distortions in bond angles and changes in bond polarities exert on the course of organic reactions. We must make new and strange molecules to see whether our notions about intra- and intermolecular forces are correct. We must develop new and powerful methods for manipulating complex molecules to duplicate in the laboratory still more complex molecules which influence and shape biological processes. And we must try to understand the processes which nature has adopted for their synthesis.

Understanding is the requisite for control. By the design of suitable chemicals, it is already possible to suppress certain diseases and pests, though, as recent events have proved, we must proceed with caution lest we create more problems than we have solved. It is not too much to expect that a thorough understanding of structural organic chemistry will eventually lead not only to an understanding of life processes but to their control.

Glossary

Acetylenes: The group of alkynes.

Acid: An electron-pair acceptor or electrophile.

Activation energy: The minimum energy over and above the energy of the average molecule which is required for a chemical change. The energy required to convert the reacting molecules from the initial state to the transition state.

Addition reaction: A reaction in which a π bond is broken.

Alcohol: An organic molecule which can be formally derived from water by replacing one of the hydrogen atoms by an organic residue.

Aldehydes: Compound containing the group $-\overset{\displaystyle H}{\overset{|}{C}}=O$.

Alicyclic hydrocarbon: A hydrocarbon whose structural formula incorporates a ring but which is not aromatic.

Aliphatic hydrocarbon: An alkane.

Alkanes: A group of organic substances having the general formula C_nH_{2n+2}.

Alkene: A hydrocarbon which contains a double bond.

Alkyne: A hydrocarbon which contains a triple bond.

Amine: A derivative of ammonia in which some or all of the hydrogens have been replaced by organic residues.

Aromatic hydrocarbon: A hydrocarbon resembling benzene in chemical behavior.

Asymmetric carbon atom: A carbon atom having four different substituents.

Asymmetric molecule: A molecule not superimposable on its mirror image.

Asymmetric synthesis: Synthesis of optically active substance.

Atomic orbital: Solution of a wave equation which describes the properties of an electron in an atom.

Base: An electron-pair donor or nucleophile.

Bond: The force which holds two atoms together in a molecule.

Bond strength: The energy released in forming a bond.

Carbanion: A relatively unstable molecule which contains negatively charged carbon.

Carbonium ion: A relatively unstable molecule which contains positively charged carbon.

Carbonyl compounds: Compounds containing a carbon-oxygen double bond.

Carboxylic acids: Compounds containing the group —COOH.

Chain reaction: A reaction which propagates itself because each of the steps produces a reactive substance which brings about the next step.

Configuration: The relative arrangement of groups attached to a central atom which cannot be altered without breaking of bonds.

Conformations: Different spatial arrangements of atoms in a molecule which can be converted into one another without the breaking of bonds.

Conjugation: Alternation of double bonds (at least two) and single bonds in an organic molecule.

Covalent bond: A bond which results from the "sharing" of electrons or overlap of orbitals.

Cyanides: Compounds containing the group —C≡N. Also called nitriles.

Delocalization: A concept which seeks to explain the properties of certain molecules, primarily those containing π electrons, by assuming the participation of electrons in the formation of more than one covalent bond.

Delocalization energy: Extra stabilization of a molecule because of electron delocalization. Same as resonance energy.

Dextrorotatory substance: An optically active substance

which has the property of rotating the plane of plane-polarized light to the right.

Diastereomers: Optical isomers which are not mirror images of each other.

Double bond: A bond comprising one σ bond and one π bond.

Electron affinity: The work required to remove an electron to an infinite distance from a negatively charged ion.

Electronegativity: The relative power of an atom in a molecule to attract electrons to itself.

Electrophile: A substance which bonds with carbon by accepting an electron pair.

Enantiomers: A pair of molecules bearing a mirror image relationship to each other.

Endothermic reaction: A reaction in the course of which heat is absorbed.

Equilbrium-controlled reaction: A reaction in which the proportion of different products depends on their relative stability.

Ether: An organic molecule which can be formally derived from water by replacing both hydrogen atoms by organic residues.

Exothermic reaction: A reaction in the course of which heat is released.

Geometric isomerism: Isomerism due to restricted rotation about double bonds, or about single bonds in alicyclic molecules.

Halogenation: The replacement of hydrogen by halogen.

Heterolysis: Cleavage of bonds in which one of the fragments retains both of the electrons which previously constituted the bond.

Homolysis: Cleavage of bonds in which each of the fragments retains one of the electrons which previously constituted the bond.

Hund rule: The rule which says that if several orbitals of equal energy are available, none is filled completely until each is occupied by at least one electron.

Hybrid orbital: An orbital formed by the linear combination of different types of atomic orbitals.

Hydrocarbon: An organic compound containing only carbon and hydrogen.

Hydrogenation: The addition of hydrogen to double or triple bonds, usually in the presence of a catalyst.

Intermediate: A relatively unstable or reactive product of a chemical reaction.

Ionic bond: The electrostatic attraction between ions of opposite charge.

Ionization potential: The work necessary to remove an electron from an atom to an infinite distance in the gaseous state.

Isomerism: The relationship between two compounds having the same molecular formula but different structures.

Isomers: Compounds having the same molecular formula but different structures.

Kinetically controlled reaction: A reaction in which the proportion of different products depends on their relative rates of formation.

Kinetics: A study of the factors affecting the rate of reaction.

Levorotatory substance: An optically active substance which has the property of rotating the plane of plane-polarized light to the left.

Mechanism: A hypothetical description of the way in which starting materials are changed into products in a given reaction.

Mercaptan: A compound containing the —SH group.

Meso isomers: A molecule containing asymmetric carbon atoms which has a plane of symmetry.

Molecular orbital: The solution of a wave equation which describes the properties of a bonding electron in a molecule.

Molecular rearrangement: A change in carbon skeleton during a reaction.

Nitration: The replacement of hydrogen by the group $—NO_2$.

Nucleophile: A substance which bonds with carbon by donating an electron pair to an electron-deficient site.

Olefin: An alkene.

Optical activity: The ability to rotate the plane of polarized light.

Optical isomers: Substances which have the same gross structure but which differ from each other in configuration.

Orbital: Solution of a wave equation which describes the properties of an electron; a measure of the region in space where this electron is likely to be found.

Ozonolysis: The reaction of an alkene or alkyne with ozone.

Pauli exclusion principle: The rule which says that an orbital can be occupied by two electrons only if the electrons have opposite spin.

π Bond: A covalent bond formed by overlap of two atomic p orbitals whose axes are parallel.

Plane-polarized light: A light beam whose advancing wavefront vibrates in one plane only perpendicular to the direction of propagation.

Polar bond: A covalent bond between two atoms of different electronegativities.

Polar molecule: A molecule which orients itself when placed in an electric field.

Polarimeter: An instrument used for measuring the angle through which a beam of plane-polarized light has been rotated.

Polarization: Distortion of electron distribution in a molecule by an outside agent.

Racemate: A mixture of equal amounts of enantiomers.

Radical: A generally unstable molecule which contains one or more unpaired electrons.

Rate: The velocity of a reaction.

Resolution: The separation of a racemate into its enantiomers.

Resonance: A concept which seeks to express the actual structure of certain molecules, primarily those containing π electrons, in terms of various contributing structures which differ from each other only in the distribution of valence electrons, but not in the distribution of atomic nuclei.

Resonance energy: The extra energy bestowed by resonance on a molecule not readily represented by a single valence bond structure. Same as delocalization energy.

Resonance hybrid: The actual structure of a molecule not readily represented by a single conventional structural formula, as expressed in terms of several contributing valence bond structures.

σ bond: A covalent bond formed by overlap of two atomic orbitals whose axes coincide. The resulting molecular orbital is cylindrically symmetrical around the line joining the atomic nuclei.

Stereomers: Substances that have the same molecular formula and the same gross structure but differ from each other in geometry or configuration.

Structural formula: A planar projection of the spatial relationship between atoms in a molecule.

Structure: The arrangement in space of atoms in a molecule.

Substitution reaction: A reaction in which one atom or group of atoms is replaced by another.

Sulfonation: The replacement of hydrogen by the group $—SO_3H$.

Transition state: A hypothetical description of reacting molecules and their relative orientation at the stage when they have acquired the activation energy necessary for the particular reaction.

Triple bond: A bond comprising one σ and two π bonds.

Wave function: The solution of a wave equation.

Suggested Readings

The student interested in learning more about nomenclature of organic compounds will find an excellent summary in the following text book:

D. J. Cram and G. S. Hammond, *Organic Chemistry*, McGraw-Hill, New York, 1959, pp. 645–667.

This book, and the ones listed below, will also afford a more detailed discussion of many topics mentioned in the preceding pages.

R. T. Morrison and R. N. Boyd, *Organic Chemistry*, Allyn and Bacon, Boston, 1959.

T. A. Geissman, *Principles of Organic Chemistry*, 2d ed., Freeman, San Francisco, 1962.

L. Fieser and M. Fieser, *Organic Chemistry*, 3d ed., Reinhold, New York, 1956.

L. Fieser and M. Fieser, *Advanced Organic Chemistry*, Reinhold, New York, 1961; a somewhat more detailed and advanced treatment of many subjects covered in the preceding book.

Many articles on organic chemistry that can be enjoyed by the person who has read the present volume are published in the *Scientific American* and the *Journal of Chemical Education.* A selection of recent ones is given.

H. C. Brown, Foundations of the Structural Theory, *J. Chem. Educ.*, **36,** 104 (1959).

E. N. Hiebert, The Experimental Basis of Kekule's Valence Theory, *J. Chem. Educ.*, **36,** 320 (1959).

A. Ihde, The Unraveling of Geometric Isomerism and Tautomerism, *J. Chem. Educ.*, **36,** 330 (1959).

C. C. Price, The Geometry of Giant Molecules, *J. Chem. Educ.*, **36,** 160 (1959).

E. L. Eliel, Conformational Analysis in Mobile Systems, *J. Chem. Educ.*, **37,** 126 (1960).

Symposium on Medicinal Chemistry, *J. Chem. Educ.*, **37,** 168–201 (1960).

W. R. Roderick, Structural Variety of Natural Products, *J. Chem. Educ.*, **39**, 2 (1962).

J. D. Roberts, Organic Chemical Reactions, *Sci. Am.*, **197**, 117 (1957).

G. Natta, How Giant Polymers are Made, *Sci. Am.*, **197**, 98 (1957).

T. Robinson, Alkaloids, *Sci. Am.*, **201**, 113 (1959).

G. Natta, Precisely Constructed Polymers, *Sci. Am.*, **205**, 33 (1961).

Index